The LIGHTING HANDBOOK

BY JOHN CULLEN

PELHAM BOOKS

First published in Great Britain by
Pelham Books Ltd
27 Wright's Lane
Kensington
London W8
1986

Designed and produced by
Johnson Editions Ltd
15 Grafton Square
London SW4 0DQ

British Library Cataloguing in Publication Data
Cullen, John
        The lighting handbook.
        1. Electric lighting 2. Interior lighting
        I. Title
        729'.28 TK4175
ISBN 0-7207-1658-6

Editor: Georgina Harding
Assistant editor: Zuza Vrbova
Designer: Lorraine Johnson
Typesetting: Fowler Printing Services
Production: Landmark Production Consultants
Origination: ScanTrans, Singapore
Printed and bound in Hong Kong by
Mandarin Offset Marketing (H.K.) Ltd.

CONTENTS

Light determines how we perceive space. Artists have long been aware of how nuances of light change appearances in nature. A slanting ray of late-afternoon sunlight highlights and casts shadows, modelling the objects on which it falls, while a bright midday sun overhead throws flat, unvaried illumination over everything. The same applies to artificial light.

The modelling potential of light has long been exploited in theatre, in photography and in cinema. These art forms have also made use of its emotional power, using shadow, tone and colour to create mood. There is no reason why domestic lighting should not do the same, in a subtle way. Artificial light thrown on to the surfaces of a room from different heights and angles can appear to alter its features and dimensions. It can emphasize height or breadth, dramatize structure and materials, becoming almost an architectural element. At different tones and intensities it can also evoke mood, inviting concentration or relaxation, coolness or warmth.

Lighting gives a dramatic backdrop to a simply furnished room. A leafy pattern is cast on the wall by low-voltage projectors fitted with shaped masks (or 'gobos'), special lenses and colour filters (see p28). Further light, from accent sources, draws attention to two decorative features — a picture and a bowl of lilies.

In the past, decorators have tended to neglect lighting, concentrating instead on the colours and patterns of fabrics and wallpapers, and the styling and arrangement of pieces of furniture. Light fittings were considered necessary yet accessory to the decorating scheme, and were usually selected as pretty objects to match the rest of the room. For many people, awareness of the quality of the light each type of fitting produced began with a negative aspect: they recognized the failings of the ubiquitous central ceiling pendant, whose light gives as little subtlety of tone and shadow as the midday sun. But if the pendant is disposed of, what can be used in its stead?

The solution lies with completely different types of light fitting. Now widely available, these fittings have brought a radical new element into interior decoration. Whereas carpets, wall-papers and furniture are solid and unchanging — at least until you sell or redecorate — interior lighting can be a plastic medium. It can be manipulated to dim and brighten, obscure and highlight, create plays of shadow and even colour. It can transform the atmosphere of a room just as theatre lighting transforms a scene.

This book gives an introduction to the use of this evocative element of decoration. First it gives a description of the basic tools and techniques, cutting through the jargon that surrounds the new lighting, and explaining what the main types of fitting are and how they are used. It then goes through the house, room by room, considering the lighting requirements of

In the author's lighting showroom, different groups of fittings are used to demonstrate how lighting can alter the atmosphere and appearance of a space. Top left. Tungsten-halogen uplighters give bold emphasis to the ceiling and upper section of the walls. Top right. Tungsten-halogen wall-washers, directed on to the left-hand wall and the back wall of the connecting room, create a cool, open feel. Bottom left. Tungsten downlighters throw soft light on to the floor. Bottom right . A mass of accent lights pinpoint objects in the room and give a starry sparkle to the ceiling.

each room as well as any special problem they pose for lighting design, and suggests appropriate schemes. The illustrations show a mass of different effects in different styles. None of the lighting schemes are prescribed. They are intended as example and inspiration. Interior lighting offers infinite room for experiment.

Developments in lighting, unlike other areas of interior decoration, are dependent on developments in technology. While today's lighting designer tends to work with light itself, creating fittings to produce chosen effects, the designers of the past had little control over the quality of the light and mostly concentrated on making decorative objects.

The illustrations below give an indication of the limitations on lighting design. The various kinds of light source used through history, from the simple oil lamps of antiquity to the gas lamps of the nineteenth century, offered little scope in terms of effect. Though a certain amount of variety could be achieved in style and ornamentation, even the forms were limited: a lamp or candlestick could only be placed on a table, fixed to the wall, set on a tall pedestal, or hung from the ceiling. Moreover it had to be within easy reach for

frequent control, adjustment and maintenance. This approach was so established that designs for electric lighting, when it arrived, copied these traditional models.

Edison's invention of the incandescent bulb — the successful trial took place on 21 October, 1879 — revolutionized lighting technology. Artificial light was suddenly possible in a clean, bright, safe, odourless and almost maintenance-free form, and one that could be easily controlled and manipulated. The first house to install electric light, in 1880, was Cragside in Northumberland, designed by Norman Shaw for the self-made millionaire Sir William Armstrong. At the time, it seemed fantastic that such luxury should ever be available to all. Besides, there was some controversy about the effects of electric light on health and eyesight, and scientists and doctors were called upon for their opinions. However,

Below. Lighting from antiquity to the Renaissance. The first source of artificial light was probably a flaming torch – the precursor of the medieval torchère (centre left). The next development was the oil lamp of the Greeks and Romans, first probably a hollow stone or shell (centre), later a purpose-made terracotta vessel (centre right). Oil lamps were supplanted by candles, which were stuck on a spike in 'pricket' candlesticks (bottom left), wall sconces and chandeliers.

Below. Lighting of the seventeenth and eighteenth centuries. The candle was the major light source, made of wax or of cheaper but foul-smelling tallow. Candlestick design became increasingly elaborate, and sconces, candelabra and chandeliers were made to hold large numbers of candles — necessary to provide adequate brightness. Small conveniences included the extinguisher and snuffler shown fitted to the portable chamber candlestick (centre right).

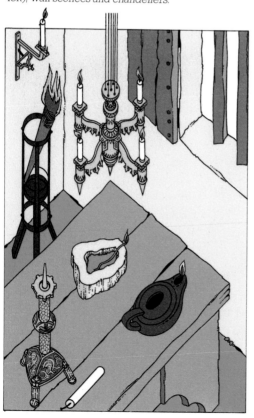

during the next twenty years electric light came to be installed in many of the better-off homes.

On the design front, new ideas developed slowly. The gas lamp, chandelier and candlestick were simply translated into electric fittings, with additional lamp-shades to conceal the unsightly bare bulb and diffuse its light. It was not until the 1920s that architects slowly came to recognize the potential of lighting as a design element. The concept of indirect lighting began to develop. Rather than place a lamp on a table to cast light immediately around it, the light could be reflected off the ceiling and dispersed around the room. The uplighter, which throws light on to the ceiling, became a prominent feature of lighting schemes during the 1920s and 1930s. At the same time, architects such as Gropius and Le Corbusier began to experiment with incorporating light into the structure of buildings,

using opaque or transparent glass walls and skylights in addition to large expanses of metal-framed window. Light fittings were designed as an integral part of buildings, and a new functionalism stripped them of ornament and laid emphasis on their effect.

For the general public, however, the traditional type of light fitting has remained a standard feature of the home. The technological and design developments of recent years have usually taken place in the fields of commercial and industrial lighting, and have slowly filtered through into domestic trends. In its purest form, today's lighting takes the concept of indirect lighting to its logical conclusion: a room where light is cast on to walls, ceilings, floor and objects by invisible sources. In terms of design, this development represents a step far greater than that from candlelight to the electric bulb.

Below. Lighting of the nineteenth century. While the candle was still common, new sources were developed: oil lamps (top left, top centre and bottom left) using a hollow wick which drew in a reservoir of oil or later, paraffin; and gas lighting, seen in the streets early in the century but not used domestically until the 1870s. Natural gas was piped to the house, with attachments for wall fittings (top right), chandeliers (far right) and table lamps (centre).

Below. Lighting from the 1900s to the 1950s — all powered by electricity. While many popular designs used traditional forms and materials, the 1920s and 1930s saw the introduction of materials such as aluminium, chrome and plastic. One early example is a standard lamp with chrome tube base and conical plastic shade (bottom right). An influential innovation was the adjustable task light (centre) with flexible metal stem and curved metal reflector.

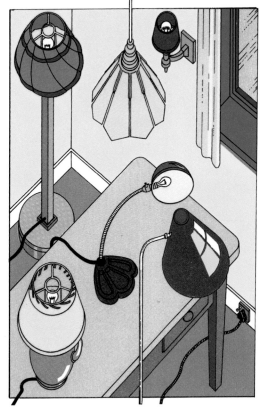

A look at the many new lighting shops today reveals a bewildering number of different light fittings. Many are beautiful objects in their own right, others are totally discreet. Where and how do you start to choose?

The answer — a surprise to many people — is not just to pick the most beautiful design. If you do this, you will in effect have made a decision to acquire another ornament or piece of furniture. Instead, decide first what lighting effect you want. Choosing an attractive fitting to generate this effect is a secondary step.

SIX CONSIDERATIONS WHEN CHOOSING YOUR LIGHTING

Imagine that you are setting out to paint your room with light. Think three-dimensionally, then try to answer the six sets of questions below. This should help to focus your attention on the fundamentals.

Space and atmosphere. Objectively assess the space to be lit. Is it a kitchen or a bedroom, a bathroom or a corridor? The garden patio or dining room? How is the space to be used? What type of ambience is most appropriate?

Form and design. What are your plans for the room? What are the main pieces of furniture and where will they be sited? What will the colour scheme be? Will there be carpets or bare floorboards, wallpaper or paint, curtains or blinds?

Focus and detail. Which are the main features to be highlighted in the room? These might be architectural or decorative, and could include cornices, fireplace, niches, fine plasterwork or panelling, paintings, sculpture, furniture, bay window or plants. You might equally consider what would be best left unlit.

Tasks. What activities to be performed in the room will require special lighting consideration? Where will you read, sew, chop vegetables, shave or make up?

Practicalities. Are there are any restrictions to the installation of new wiring? For example, do the walls or ceilings consist of concrete, or is there access to the ceiling from the floor above?

Control. Finally, technical details must be considered. Where do you want your control? How many switches and power points do you need in the room? Do you want dimmers, and how many different circuits are needed?

BASIC TYPES OF ILLUMINATION

Whatever style you decide on, and whichever kinds of fittings you favour, thought must be given to three basic types of lighting. First, general lighting provides overall brightness in the space. Second, task lighting gives adequate light for specific needs such as study, reading or sewing. Third, accent lighting adds decorative highlights, drawing the eye to special features in the room. Some rooms in the house may use only one or two of these types of lighting, but the complex function of an area such as a living room will probably require them all.

In the past, traditional fittings have been used in all three ways, obvious examples being a pendant, a desk light and a picture light. Sometimes the sources have been doubled up in terms of function; for example, a table lamp, if placed at a sufficient height, will provide adequate general lighting and a good reading or task source at the same time.

Today's new breed of fittings, however, have been designed to do these jobs with much greater precision. Using them as tools you can

bring light exactly where you want it. For example, general illumination need no longer mean lighting several surfaces within the room simultaneously, as with the conventional pendant. Instead, it is possible to choose to emphasize the floor, the ceiling or the walls by lighting them quite separately, and the single brightly lit surface will reflect adequate overall light back into the room. Each effect gives a definite form to a space, form which can be varied from area to area, and even in a single space through the course of the day and evening. Here lies the key to transforming a room with light. Compared with the possibilities of a single pendant, one or two table lamps and perhaps a single picture light, the opportunities are very exciting indeed.

The use of a variety of light sources at different intensities gives many facets to the character of this unusual sitting room, photographed here from three different angles. Opposite left. By day the room seems wide and airy. Opposite right. By night it is given dramatic height by low-voltage uplighters concealed in the ledge behind the sofa, making a bold vertical feature of the mirror frame; a downlighter gives contrasting, low-level emphasis on the coffee table. Top right. The use of downlighters at higher intensity over the entire floor area gives a bright, open impression, more akin to the daytime atmosphere. Bottom right. With downlighters off, except for one low-voltage source above the coffee table, tungsten-halogen uplighters (concealed above the corner cupboards) dimmed to low intensity, and low-voltage accent sources trained on to pictures and ornaments, the room seems small and intimate. All these effects are produced by careful control of judiciously selected fittings. The techniques used could be applied to almost any space.

Downlighters are fittings designed to direct light straight downwards. If they are carefully arranged as an array in the ceiling, the effect is to evenly illuminate the horizontal surface below. Just as with all other types of fitting, many varieties exist and versions are available for surface-mounting on the ceiling and for setting halfway or completely within the ceiling void. Wall-mounted downlighters are available for use over counters and sideboards. Needless to say, floor-mounted downlighters do not exist.

The very simplest form of downlighter is a tin can containing an ordinary GLS bulb (see *Bulb Chart* pp88-89). This is not, however, a very efficient light source: while some light would indeed emanate downwards, most would merely be absorbed in the can.

Above. An array of recessed downlighters creates an even distribution of light, contributing to the atmosphere of this unusual, double-height space. Placed close to the wall of the gallery, the fittings produce a pattern of scallops of light, that, besides being pleasing, also effectively accentuate the pictures. Note the contrast in colour between tungsten light and natural daylight.

There are two ways in which proper downlighters overcome this problem. One kind uses reflector bulbs such as the PAR 38, the range of ISL reflector bulbs, or the new multi-mirror low-voltage sources. All these bulbs incorporate their own reflectors to direct the light downwards. Thus the downlighter fitting itself is only a means of housing the bulb and, in most cases, providing glare control.

More sophisticated downlighters incorporate a reflector as part of the fitting and therefore use simpler 'bare' bulbs such as the GLS. These fittings may cost more initially as a result of their reflector component, but the GLS bulbs are much cheaper to replace than reflector bulbs. Moreover, inbuilt downlighter reflectors are usually carefully designed, often by computer, to make the most efficient use of the bulb, restrict glare and produce a defined beam of light. Reflectors are available with either silver or gold finishes, silver leaving the colour of the light unchanged, gold producing a warmer-coloured output. The gold effect is particularly suitable for interiors with a brown or beige colour scheme; the yellower light intensifies the depth of these colours and helps to create a very warm and inviting atmosphere.

A new generation of downlighters, also incorporating their own reflectors, take highly efficient compact fluorescent bulbs. These offer very economical and long-lasting lighting – the Thorn 2D bulb, for example, has a rated life of 5,000 hours as opposed to 1,000 hours for the GLS. One drawback to these fittings, however, is that they cannot be dimmed.

A related type of light source is the 'eyeball' fitting, technically described as a semi-recessed directional downlighter. This is similar in principle to a fully recessed downlighter but has a spherical base which can be swivelled in its socket — as the name suggests — so that light is directed at an angle, as from a spotlight. Eyeballs fulfil a dual function. Pointed directly downwards they perform exactly like downlighters. Pointed on to walls or objects they can be used like spotlights to provide a narrow, specific accent beam or a wider beam that gives a mix of accent and general light.

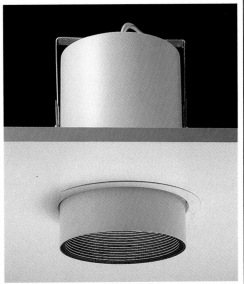

INSTALLATION

All recessed downlighters — and recessed fittings generally — are attached by some form of clip and spring fixing which holds them in place in a hole cut for them in the ceiling. The actual mechanism varies from one design to another. These fixings are suitable for most types of ceiling, including plasterboard and plaster set into expanded metal. They can also be used in older lath-and-plaster ceilings, although care should be taken beforehand to ensure that the ceiling is not in too decrepit a condition. The depth required will vary from around 10cm/4in for a low-voltage fitting to around 30cm/12in, depending on the type of bulb used.

Where the ceiling void is not sufficiently deep for a fully recessed fitting, it may be possible to use a semi-recessed one. Failing that, or if you have a solid ceiling, it will be necessary to use a surface-mounted fitting.

Top. Fully recessed downlighter. Centre. Variable-depth downlighter. Bottom. Eyeball or semi-recessed directional downlighter.

PLANNING AN ARRAY

One single downlighter placed centrally over a coffee table or console will provide very effective local illumination but will not illuminate an entire room. For general lighting it is necessary to have an array of downlighters across the ceiling. The number and spacing of the array will depend on the beam angle of the selected fitting and how much surface area it will illuminate.

Beam angle is technically defined as twice the angle between the centre of the light beam and the point where the light level drops to one half the intensity at the centre (see diagram). To estimate accurately the area which will be covered by a downlighter, make a simple scale drawing of ceiling and floor and use a protractor to draw in the beam angle. When planning the array, bear in mind that light of lower intensity will in fact spill over the edge of the specified beam angle. This makes it possible to arrange downlighters so that the output of each one merges with that of the next. It is essential to ensure that the beams overlap in this way if they are to provide comfortable general illumination; if the outputs are too separated, the effect will be very patchy.

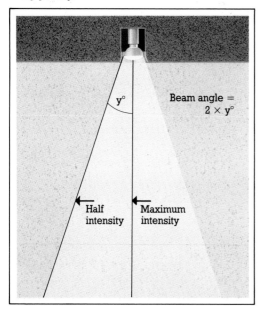

Above. The edges of a beam of light from any fitting are designated as points where the light intensity is half the maximum intensity at the beam's centre.

In the case of high-quality downlighters with integral reflectors, the beam angle of each fitting will always be specified by the manufacturer. For downlighters using reflector bulbs, the beam angle will correspond to that of the bulb. This can be checked in the *Bulb Chart* (see pp88-89).

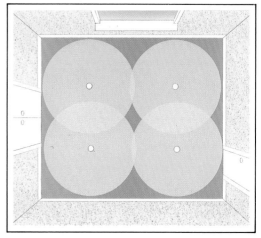

Above. Beams of light arranged in groups should merge into one another to create an even effect.

The wattage of the fittings will depend on the intensity of general illumination required. This should take into account the colour of the floor, since it is this surface which acts as a reflector, providing light more generally for the entire space. A dark carpet reflects virtually no light at all, whereas white or beige flooring may be expected to reflect as much as 70 per cent of the light it receives. The height of the ceiling also affects the ultimate result: the higher it is, the less light reaches the floor.

The amount of light falling on any surface is measured in terms of *lux*. Given all the colours of walls, floor and ceiling, the room height and the use of the space, most manufacturers or specialist lighting designers will be able to calculate exactly the wattages and number of fittings required. However, such precise calculations are not usually necessary. The table below gives a very approximate guide.

Guide to fittings required for general illumination in living room (light colour scheme)

Dimensions of room	Ceiling height		
	2·5m/8ft or less	2.5–3m/ 8–10ft	3–4m/ 10–13ft
2·5 × 3m/ 8 × 10ft	6 × 60 watt	4 × 100 watt	4 × 150 watt
3·5 × 4·5m/ 12 × 14ft	10 × 60 watt	6 × 100 watt	6 × 150 watt
5 × 6m/ 16 × 20ft	14 × 60 watt	9 × 100 watt	9 × 150 watt

Having arrived at the type, wattage, beam angle and quantity of downlighters you require, make a final check to ensure that the ones you have selected offer some form of glare control around the bulb inside. A number of the more inexpensive fittings on the market bring the bulb

Above. Recessed ceiling-mounted spill-ring downlighters eliminate any glare from the white surfaces in this bathroom. Right. Cross-section of a spill-ring downlighter in situ. This fitting incorporates two reflectors instead of the usual one so that the bulb is completely hidden.

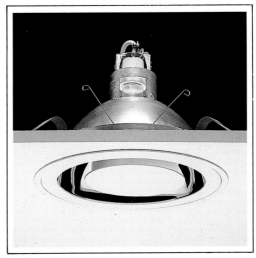

right down to the bottom level of casing. This provides no shield for the bulb whatsoever. Whilst these fittings may be satisfactory for cupboards or for small utility areas, any dramatic downlighting effect will be spoilt by glare from multiple lamps across the ceiling.

Downlighting may seem complicated in theory. In fact, it is not difficult in practice and with a little observation one can soon pick up an idea of the effects that are possible. A golden rule when selecting a downlighter — or any light fitting — is to arrange to see it working first and assess its effect in terms of both beam angle and brightness. The eye alone can often make a surprisingly quick and accurate judgement.

Wall-washers are ceiling-mounted fittings designed to cast light evenly across and down a wall. As opposed to downlighters and uplighters, they place emphasis on the vertical surface rather than the floor or ceiling — breadth rather than height or depth. They can also contribute to the general lighting of the space by using the wall as a reflector. As with downlighting, the paler the colour of the reflecting surface, the more light is reflected into the room.

The use of wall-washers is more limited than that of downlighters or uplighters. Firstly, the effect requires a large stretch of clear wall space in order to produce adequate general lighting on its own. Secondly, by emphasizing a wall, wall-washing may make it seem to advance. This is inadvisable in small rooms.

They come into their own, however, when used either to emphasize the architectural form or texture of a wall surface or to brightly illuminate a mural or a mass of pictures. Here a well-designed wall-washer provides completely even illumination down the entire wall, with a sharp cut-off of light at the junction of wall and ceiling. Very little illumination falls into the main body of the floor space. In contrast, a downlighter placed adjacent to the wall would produce a definite 'scallop' of light down the wall and cast most of its illumination on to the floor.

These technical characteristics should be borne in mind when buying wall-washers. Beware of the current tendency in some lighting shops to describe as a wall-washer any source which is capable of angling light at the wall. This is a far cry from the true wall-wash effect.

Wall-washers are similar in construction to downlighters, with either a reflector bulb or a GLS bulb and separate reflector within a curved housing. However an additional reflector of some type must be included in the wall-washer in order to restrict its output to one direction only. Often a broadly curved 'scoop' reflector is also added to ensure that the light reaches the very top of the wall. Of necessity, almost all wall-washers are ceiling-mounted. Common bulb types are the same as those for downlighters, i.e. GLS, PAR 38 and the family of ISL bulbs, although some particularly powerful wall-washers are available which take the linear tungsten-halogen bulb (see pp88-89). The majority of wall-washers take 60, 100 and 150 watt bulbs, though the more sophisticated types tend only to take 100 and 150 watt bulbs. Very often the casings of these fittings have been designed to match a downlighter fitting exactly, allowing for a combination of wall-washing and downlighting within one space.

Right top. Track-mounted 'scoop' wall-washer using GLS bulb. Centre. Recessed cone wall-washer using GLS bulb; note the extra reflector at one side to produce the wall-wash effect. Bottom. Track-mounted halogen wall-washer.

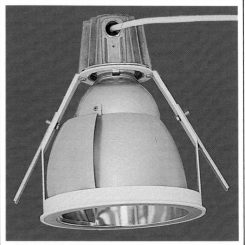

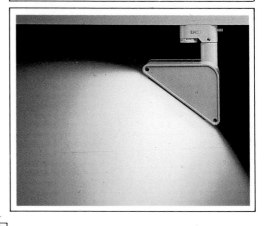

Positioning is critical since the spacing between one wall-washer and the next must ensure even distribution of light. The distance at which the wall-washers are set back from the wall must also be adjusted carefully. If they are too far out towards the centre of the ceiling, there is a risk that people may cross into the path of the beam, being dazzled and creating shadows at the same time. On average, the fittings should be placed 80–100cm /31–39in from the wall, and the space between each fitting and the next should not exceed twice the distance from the wall.

These rules for positioning will determine the number of fittings required to cover a wall. The

Above. A tungsten-halogen surface-mounted wall-washer brightly illuminates the portrait on the wall at the same time as providing general light for the room, while a row of recessed wall-washers evenly light the bookshelves.

total wattage sufficient to produce adequate general light can be estimated according to the wattage chart for downlighters (see p14).

The only exceptions to the formula are wall-washers that take linear tungsten-halogen bulbs. These cover approximately double the width of wall illuminated by a GLS or reflector bulb fitting; as a result, only half as many fittings need be installed.

The purpose of uplighters, as their name suggests, is to direct light upwards on to the ceiling. The effect is to create a sense of space and height at the same time as providing general light reflected from the ceiling surface.

Uplighters offer greater flexibility than downlighters in that fittings of different bulb types and wattages are available for fixing almost anywhere: wall-mounted, suspended from the ceiling on a stem, or freestanding — the last giving you the opportunity to achieve interesting illumination simply from a portable, plug-in source.

In terms of the bulbs they use, uplighters for general lighting fall into two categories: those designed for the new tungsten-halogen and metal-halide bulbs, and those using the more traditional GLS or tungsten reflector bulb.

Tungsten-halogen bulbs are very powerful: watt for watt they produce nearly double the output of conventional tungsten or 'incandescent' bulbs. They operate in a similar way, containing a tungsten filament which gives off light when it is heated electrically. However, the inclusion of halogen gases within the bulb envelope — not present in an ordinary tungsten bulb — sets up a special cycle which results in a much brighter output. Thus a tungsten-halogen bulb can be made much smaller yet produce the same amount of light as a tungsten bulb of higher

Below. Sculptural plaster uplighters with GLS bulbs give a pleasing though not powerful light.

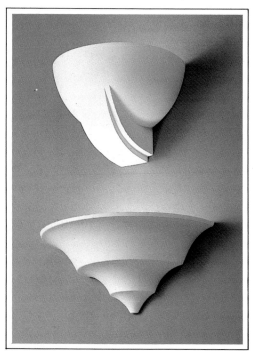

wattage. And correspondingly, a high-wattage tungsten-halogen bulb can produce a far higher level of illumination than its tungsten equivalent. For example, a single uplighter with a 300-watt, linear tungsten-halogen bulb and an efficient reflector can be enough to dramatically flood a ceiling 3–4m/10–13ft square.

The output of a tungsten-halogen bulb is also much whiter than that of a tungsten bulb, extremely crisp and sharp, and giving very faithful colour rendering. For this reason, halogen bulbs were first widely used in art galleries, museums and photographers' studios, although their special quality is now becoming more widely appreciated for the home, and seems particularly suited to the clean lines and colours of modern interiors.

Halogen bulbs can be used with dimmers, but when they are dimmed the halogen cycle stops and the bulbs act in a similar way to ordinary tungsten bulbs; their light becomes yellower in tone, and a black deposit accumulates gradually in the envelope as in an aged tungsten bulb. Manufacturers recommend that all halogen bulbs are occasionally burned at full power to allow the cycle to re-establish itself.

The type of halogen bulb most often used in uplighters is the linear one, which runs on normal mains voltage. There is also a tubular version, again mains-voltage, which is less commonly used and tends to be more expensive. The standard wattages available are 150, 200, 300 and 500 watts. Care must be taken in installation of the higher wattage bulbs, however, because of the considerable heat they produce. Do not position uplighters with bulbs in excess of 200 watts less than 1m/3ft below the ceiling and direct them away from curtains or other inflammable surfaces and materials. And because of their extreme brightness, always fix wall-mounted uplighters above eye-level and avoid placing them near the foot of a staircase or on a wall below a flight of stairs where they may glare in the eyes of someone coming down.

Even more efficient than tungsten-halogen are metal-halide bulbs, and a range of uplighters with these bulbs is rapidly coming on the market. However, these are important mainly in meeting the growing need for new uplighter techniques in offices. In the home, such high efficiency is rarely called for. Besides, the slightly blue output of metal-halide sources and the fact that they cannot be dimmed somewhat restrict their decorative possibilities.

Uplighters that take standard GLS and reflector bulbs tend to be far less powerful. With most such fittings, just one or two would scarcely be enough to illuminate a ceiling. This is not necessarily a drawback, however, since many of the designs are attractive to look at, besides providing effective lighting. For example, a

number of wall-mounted quarter-sphere fittings around the walls of a room can both wash the ceiling with light and provide interesting visual features in themselves.

A more discreet type of uplighter is the floor-standing drum; it is generally a cylinder, no more than 10–20cm/4–8in high, often kept concealed behind furniture or beneath a plant. The most usual types of bulbs for this fitting are the PAR 38 or ISL reflector bulbs; some versions however contain their own reflector and take a 40 or 100 watt crown-silvered bulb. Because of their low intensity, drum uplighters are primarily intended for accent rather than for general lighting.

Above. A symmetrical pair of tungsten-halogen uplighters give a dramatic white light to this modern room. A miniature low-voltage narrow-beam spotlight on a corner of the pedestal acts as another uplighter, highlighting the sculpture and casting its shadow up the wall.

Style and form have had considerably more impact on uplighter design generally than is seen for downlighters and wall-washers — hardly surprising since an uplighter by definition cannot be concealed in the ceiling. As a result, hundreds of varieties exist, in styles ranging from Art Deco to high tech, and one can be found to match almost any kind of decorating scheme.

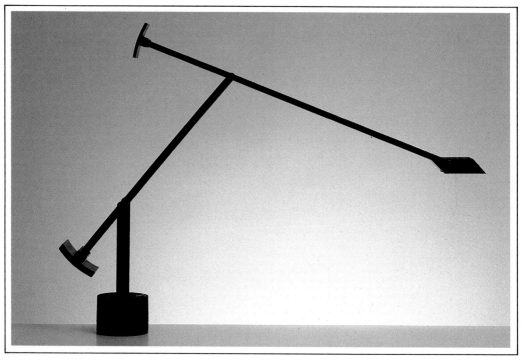

Above. Besides providing a bright enough setting for reading, the sleek, insect-like 'Tizio' light can also be pointed at the wall to produce more subtle, reflected light.

The function of a task light is self-evident, though its characteristics will differ according to the task in hand. A good reading light may also be suitable for darning but not for using the sewing machine; it might serve for sketching but not for painting; and it almost certainly will not be appropriate for making pastry or scrutinizing your face in the bathroom mirror. In each case, the one common requirement is that the lamp should provide strong local illumination exactly where it is needed to facilitate whatever activity is taking place.

In some cases, such as reading in the living room, it would be possible to arrange for the general lighting to give a sufficiently high level of illumination. This would effectively mean a light level in the order of 500 lux — equivalent to modern office lighting — and one would certainly be able to read perfectly well. However, the whole space would be brightly lit throughout, which would hardly give a restful atmosphere for late-evening reading.

Instead, task lights offer high intensity lighting without high general illumination. Their inclusion in a lighting scheme provides the required practical lighting and leaves you free to vary the general and accent lighting according to the atmosphere desired.

These pages show just a few of the innumerable task lights available. More examples can be found throughout the rest of the book. Look at them and decide what you like. There are no rules to task lighting. All that is required is common sense and a little style.

Below. The 'Pausania' light has an Art Deco look and is made from typically 1930s materials but is actually modern in design, taking the highly practical PL11 fluorescent bulb.

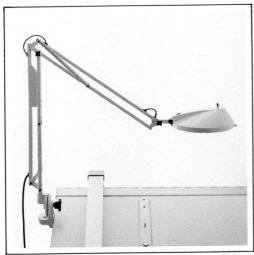

Lights to adjust to suit the task. Above. New-look, clamp-on Anglepoise taking the fluorescent Thorn 2D bulb. Above right. Adjustable-head reading light with high intensity, low-voltage, ultra-narrow halogen beam. Below. Versatile floor-based light with adjustable arm and head, made in tungsten and tungsten-halogen versions. Below right. A pair of slender floor-standing lights, giving a precise, low-voltage beam; they are operated by convenient switches on the floor.

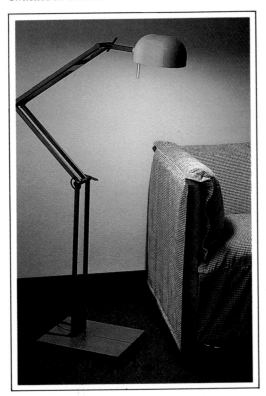

Accent sources give local rather than general illumination. Their uses are many and varied but fall into two basic categories: to make visual focal points of centres such as a coffee table or dining area, or to emphasize paintings, flowers or special objects in the room. They are supplementary to the general light sources and thus accenting is often planned as an overlay to the general lighting scheme.

This kind of illumination covers a multitude of different effects, each produced by a different type of fitting. Traditional accent sources are standard picture lights, the occasional wall bracket, strip-lamps over bookshelves. Even a simple table lamp can provide accent if used independently of the general lighting scheme. Downlighters, uplighters and wall-washers can also become accent lights.

Most accent sources are directional in their construction so that their output can be pointed

Above. Atmospheric accent from a number of sources: drum uplighters beneath plants, semi-recessed directional downlighters above pictures, and a narrow-beam fitting (unseen) over the coffee table. The output of the table lamps is restricted by the use of crown-silvered bulbs.

exactly where it is needed. The range of such sources encompasses semi-recessed eyeball fittings, surface- and track-mounted spotlights, together with fully-recessed directional fittings.

BEAM ANGLE AND POSITIONING

The term 'spotlight' loosely describes hundreds of different types of purpose-designed accent sources. When choosing a spotlight, it is essential to assess the exact characteristics of each fitting and especially the beam angle. For example, a wide-beam spotlight used to light a small watercolour would result merely in adding

to the general lighting of the room, leaving the intended feature looking lost in an expanse of brightly lit wall. For best results, it is wise to try to restrict the beam within the outline of the object to be featured rather than allowing too much light to spill over the edges. Precision highlighting is the aim for dramatic lighting schemes.

To accent a picture or any wall-mounted feature, the general rule is to position the light source between the viewer and the wall. The fitting must be placed at a suitable distance for its beam to cover the picture, and not so far that the viewer crosses into the path of the light, with the ensuing problems of shadow and glare. This effectively means that most directional accent fittings within the home should be positioned only 80–100cm/31–39in from the wall. It is a good idea to construct a simple scale sketch of the wall, ceiling and picture in order to check on the likely effect of the type of accent light you have in mind. Using a protractor, sketch the coverage of the beam, measuring half the beam angle equally either side of a line drawn to the centre of the picture (see diagram). This simple process is similar to that for assessing the correct beam angle for downlighters (see p14). As the light is directed at an angle, however, it is more important to carry out this step for accent lighting, since coverage will vary depending on how high or low on the wall the picture is hanging. Remember that the beam angle represents only the point at which light falls off by 50 per cent of the intensity at the centre; illumination will not stop dead at the edge of the beam angle. For this reason it is wise to keep the entire beam as shown on your drawing within the confines of the picture.

One last important point. Check that the spotlight you have chosen is actually capable of being tilted to the angle you require. Most recessed directional fittings allow for an angle of tilt up to 40° from the vertical, which is sufficient for most purposes.

Above. Spotlights suitable for a variety of purposes. Left. Fitting for ISL reflector bulb, giving a beam angle of around 70°. Centre. Crown-silvered 100 watt bulb with parabolic reflector giving a beam angle of around 25°. Right. Miniature fitting with 40 watt crown-silvered bulb giving a beam angle of around 15°.

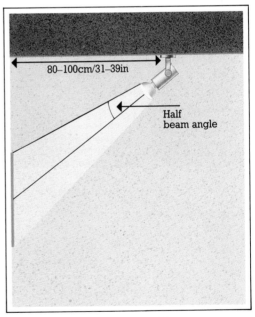

80–100cm/31–39in

Half beam angle

Above. A scale drawing will enable you to assess the beam angle required to light a picture and accurately position the fitting.

Many other types of accent source also exist, such as special lighting for shelving and niches, and uplighters for plants. These fittings cover the whole range from GLS and reflector bulbs to the newer low-voltage types. Depicted here are a few of the fittings most commonly used for accent lighting. Many more are described and pictured in use around the house elsewhere in this book.

As we have seen, the character and design of any kind of light fitting is fundamentally determined by the type of bulb it takes, be the fitting recessed, surface- or track-mounted, wall-mounted or freestanding. The development of a different type of bulb opens up new possibilities in terms of both style and effect. Low-voltage bulbs are a prime example of this. Operating on an electricity supply of only 12 or 24 volts rather than mains voltage supply of 240 volts in the UK/ 100 volts in the USA, they are a fraction of the size of conventional bulbs — the smallest measure as little as 10 or 20mm/⅜ or ⅞in in length. This offers two important advantages for fitting design: firstly, the fitting itself can be correspondingly reduced in size, and secondly, it is possible to obtain far more precise optical control from the reflectors around the tiny bulb.

Almost any type of fitting can be made in a low-voltage version. There are low-voltage downlighters with a very exact beam for accent use or a wider beam for general illumination.

Above. Ceiling-mounted low-voltage directional fittings produce hard-focused illumination of pictures, a bold form of accenting the simple modern paintings and primary colours. To achieve this hard-edged effect, it is necessary to use spotlights that have integral lenses.

There are low-voltage task lights, in which the bulb offers the benefit of precision and at the same time gives the designer scope to invent new shapes — the now-classic 'Tizio' light (see p20) with its insect-like jointed arm and small head being just one example. Generally, low-voltage bulbs lend themselves particularly well to accent lighting, where emphasis should be on the object featured and the light source is required to be as discreet as possible. There are innumerable different low-voltage accent sources, including spots, eyeballs and fully-recessed fittings.

Many of the low-voltage bulbs on the market operate on the tungsten-halogen principle and combine their small size with all the advantages of the tungsten-halogen linear lamp (see p18). These bulbs are very economical in energy terms, sometimes producing two or three times more output for equivalent wattage than a standard light source. They provide excellent colour rendering and their crisp, white output is perfect for illumination of paintings. Generally, because of their low wattage, low-voltage bulbs give off less heat, a bonus for safety and an advantage for lighting flowers and delicate objects. They also have a long life, of around 2,000 hours.

Two types of low-voltage tungsten-halogen bulb exist. Some are completely 'bare', rather like a miniature version of the GLS bulb; these require a reflector within the fitting to direct their output. Many others, particularly those known as multi-mirror bulbs, have a reflector around them as an integral part of the bulb itself. Manufactured by Thorn in the UK and General Electric in the USA, these bulbs are becoming available in an ever-increasing range of wattages and beam angles. Wattages vary from 20 watts to 75 watts, and beam angles from only 6° to over 40°. Many multi-mirror bulbs are also described as dichroic. This means that most of their heat output is passed backwards rather than into the direct path of the light. This again can be an important factor for the lighting of delicate subjects.

One distinct advantage for planning lighting is that the same fitting can be used with a wide range of different multi-mirror bulbs. This means

Above. Tiny low-voltage tungsten-halogen dichroic bulbs compared with a mains-voltage PAR 38.

that critical decisions over exact sizes of the objects to be accented need not be a worry in the initial lighting plan; only their intended positions need to be known. The fittings can be installed early on, the bulbs added at a later stage when everything else is in place; and if one day you need to change an illuminated picture for a larger one, you can simply exchange the bulb for one with a wider beam angle and insert it in the existing fitting. The fact that only one type of fitting need be used for all accenting also keeps the appearance of the ceiling consistent and uncluttered.

Below. Low-voltage fittings can produce a very precise beam, as demonstrated here. Left. Track-mounted low-voltage spotlight. Right. Fully recessed low-voltage downlighter. Both these fittings must be used with remote transformers.

TRANSFORMERS

Because low-voltage sources run on an electricity supply far below mains voltage, every low-voltage fitting requires a small device called a transformer to step down the voltage as supplied in the home to 12 or 24 volts as necessary.

Transformers, or 'adaptors', are used in many household appliances such as radios, food mixers, electric razors and so on. In these cases they are usually contained within the appliance. In the case of lighting fixtures however they may or may not be incorporated within the fitting.

Low-voltage spotlights which do incorporate an integral transformer are obviously larger than those without. Even so they are still very much smaller and neater than their mains-voltage equivalents. A small 20-watt low-voltage spotlight with integral transformer may be only 10-12cm/4-5in long and 5cm/2in in diameter.

On the other hand, fittings which rely on a remote transformer may measure no more than a few centimetres in any direction. They are also cheaper to buy than those with integral transformers. Another advantage is that a single transformer may be used to power several fittings on the same circuit, provided that they all use the same voltage. Obviously, this represents a further saving in the purchase of equipment. Remote transformers can be housed in a cupboard, in the ceiling void if a special trap is made for access, outside the room if this is more practical or even in the garage.

You will need professional advice on the use of remote transformers. An individual transformer should be of equivalent capacity (defined as *va* rating) to the wattage of the bulbs used in the fitting; a group transformer should have a *va*

Above. The lighting of these glass vases demonstrates the different effects produced by low-voltage sources with different beam angles. While wide-beam sources (left) light the overall form of the display, narrow-beam sources (right) concentrate their light in the centre of the vases so that they appear to be lit from within.

rating at least equal to the sum total of the wattages of the bulbs it is powering. Certain technicalities and regulations also apply to installation, most involving relationships between the distance from the transformer site to the fittings and the type of cable used in their connection.

Do not be put off by these restrictions. The advantages of a neat system such as this are great, and your electrical contractor, staff at one of the growing number of specialist lighting shops, or even the fitting manufacturer will help you take care of all the details.

Opposite top. Two fittings using the low-voltage multi-mirror bulb; each requires a recess opening of only 77mm/3in. Left. Fully recessed directional downlighter. Right. Recessed downlighter with dome reflector, capable of producing a wide beam like that from a mains-voltage fitting but with the advantages of small size and low heat output. Below. An individual low-voltage, narrow-beam source set immediately behind each piece of Lalique glass produces an almost surreal effect. A low-voltage spotlight is trained on the picture above. In each case, the distinct, white beams of light from these low-voltage sources demonstrate their suitability for accent use: they provide very precise highlighting, releasing little stray light to divert attention from the featured objects.

A general rule in accent lighting is that the light source is unobtrusive and correspondingly that the object it lights becomes the sole focus of attention. An entirely different approach is to use the light itself as the ornament. Modern lighting technology offers special effects that can be activated at a touch of a switch, adding a vibrant decorative element, or even a touch of theatre, to the room.

A variety of lighting possibilities that have actually been gleaned from the techniques of theatre lighting can now be applied in the home, usually in a simplified form and using less bulky fittings. One such effect is the use of coloured filters and bulbs. Many standard domestic bulbs, particularly PAR 38 and ISL bulbs, are available in a limited range of colours, and many fittings can be fitted with coloured filters which simply clip on to the frame. Sheets of colour filter — often referred to as *gels* — are available from theatrical lighting suppliers and come in literally hundreds of different shades and tones.

A more sophisticated theatre technique is the use of projectors similar to framing projectors (see p47) to project colours and images on to walls, floors and ceilings. As with a framing projector, the light is projected through a mask — known as a *gobo* in the theatre. But instead of being cut to the shape of a picture or sculpture, the gobo is cut to outline an image — leaves or clouds perhaps, or an abstract pattern (see illustration on p6). Some types of projector incorporate a motor so that the projected image can also be made to move round slowly.

Other effects, more evocative of Hollywood, can be created using rows of small light bulbs. Clear plastic tubing containing a series of miniature low-voltage bulbs, only 6mm/¼in square, are available from specialist lighting shops. This tubing can be set into the steps of a staircase, giving a touch of glamour and at the same time fulfilling the practical function of clearly defining each tread — particularly useful for safety where a change of level occurs unexpectedly in a dim hall or landing. The plastic strips can also be attached to walls, made into chandeliers or hung side by side across an opening, like bead curtains.

A do-it-yourself alternative that produces a similar sparkle is to use rows of mains-voltage bulbs. These are fitted into ordinary brass bulb-holders that have been set on a wooden batten. The effect, commonly seen alongside mirrors, could also be used at the edge of a raised floor or along a cornice as in the examples here. Small golf-ball bulbs are particularly useful for this, and low wattages must be used to avoid glare and excessive heat. Softer light can be achieved by adding an acrylic strip above the bulbs as a diffuser (see illustration on p63).

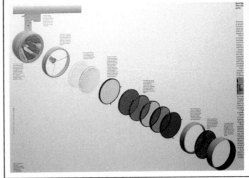

Opposite top. A row of golf-ball bulbs makes a glittering cornice and also gives soft general light. Above. In this spectacular room, golf-ball bulbs are set beneath a step so that they shine on the polished pine planks below. Spotlights provide overall light, which is reflected brilliantly off white furnishings. Striking shading is achieved by directing two spotlights (unseen) diagonally on to the pinned-back curtains. Opposite bottom. Blue colour filters on downlighters give atmospheric overall illumination which is contrasted by the white splashes of light from accent sources. (For the effect without filters, see p24.) Right. Accessories for this low-voltage, track-mounted spotlight include five colour filters as well as a variety of lenses, diffusers and baffles.

Above. A ring of neon in three pale colours echoes the form of a ceiling rose. Left. A slim neon tube imitates a cornice moulding.

NEON

Another special effect, neon, is derived from advertising hoardings. The vivid colours of neon signs have been familiar on city streets since the 1920s. Only since the 1960s, however, have neon tubes that are suitable for domestic interior use been widely developed. Domestic neon tubes are of lower ampage and thus brightness than display neon, and have smaller, neater electrodes and transformers.

The term neon lighting is commonly applied, though inaccurately, to cold cathode lighting — decorative lighting produced by tubes containing neon or argon gas. Neon, when used alone, emits the bright orange-red light associated with display signs. Argon emits a blue light. Using phosphors like those used to colour fluorescent tubes, plus coloured glass, it is possible to obtain 25 or more different colours from these two sources, including reds, pinks and oranges and bright and pastel blues, greens and yellows as well as plain white. The fittings operate on very high voltage and so require transformers and special kinds of cable; safer fittings using a low-voltage input are only now being developed.

Above. A neon cactus makes a witty addition to the plants in this conservatory-like window.

However, this lighting is very economical in terms of electricity, and will last indefinitely if properly used.

Neon lighting can be shaped into surprising conversation pieces. It is possible to buy off-the-peg neon palm trees, cocktail glasses, even cats, all with built-in transformers so that they can simply be plugged into a 13-amp socket. For a more architectural effect, it is also possible to buy custom-made neon ornaments. For example, a slim neon tube can be formed into an illuminated cornice or ceiling rose, as here.

A living room is exactly what it says it is: a place to be lived in rather than a work-room, study or bedroom. And 'living' covers a multitude of different moods and occupations, both social and solitary. This is worth emphasizing because many people approach the problem of how to light a living room by paying attention only to specific needs — placing a reading light by a favourite armchair, another source above the drinks cabinet, another beside the record-player, without any overall concept. Too often the resulting lighting is functional but devoid of atmosphere.

The main criterion of any living room is that it should be a relaxing, inviting space, flexible for all that goes on there but nevertheless with a definite style. The lighting design must fulfil the same requirements. If it is well planned the lighting itself will lend the room a unified character, linking the different focuses of activity. Specific lighting, therefore, should never be allowed to dominate the scheme.

Below. In stark contrast to the oak beams of this converted barn, modern low-voltage, track-mounted spotlights produce stunning swathes of light along the walls and floor. The shadows in between help to create a cosy atmosphere by breaking up the large expanse.

General and accent lighting should be decided first; task lights can be added afterwards.

For general lighting, it is possible to use any of the four basic alternatives — downlighting, uplighting, wall-washing or the traditional arrangement of table, wall, standard and pendant fittings. In practice, a combination of two or even more of these types may provide the best solution, balancing architectural, practical and other considerations. Unless the room is very large, however, it is unwise to mix too many different types of fitting; a plethora of different light sources will fail to produce a coherent impression.

Whichever scheme you settle upon, it must have the capacity to produce a sufficiently high level of light to compensate for lack of natural light on overcast days and to give brightness when it is needed, as well as giving a softer atmosphere for evenings. Most of the fittings available for general lighting can be fitted with dimmers. Thus you should set out to select fittings that can give the highest level of illumination ever to be required, and at the same time ensure that some form of dimming is included in the scheme (see pp86-87). The ability to adjust the general lighting will allow you to change the atmosphere of the room.

TRADITIONAL FITTINGS

The conventional lighting plan for a living area is an arrangement of portable table and standard lamps, or a combination of these with wall brackets and chandelier or other pendant. The result — miraculous though it may have seemed at the dawn of electricity — is illumination that is perfectly adequate but lacking in atmosphere.

Table and standard lamps

It is easy when planning a scheme with traditional lamps to be seduced by the ornamental value of each fitting and fail to consider its quality as a light source. A collection of richly coloured china lamp bases with fabric shades can create an evocative English-country look, by day as much as by night. However, the light produced by each lamp receives only the most elementary control from the shade, and it is hard to predict the overall effect. If enough lamps are used, some charm will be derived simply from the blend of light from different sources — multiplicity, as ever, being the key to successful lighting. But too often the effect can be patchy and incoherent, dividing the room into dissociated settings of tables and chairs.

More control over the output of each lamp can be achieved by thoughtful choice of shade. A conventional fabric or paper shade works in three ways: it throws light directly upwards to the ceiling, where it is rather ineffectually reflected back into the room; it casts light downwards on to the table top or floor; and it

Above. The circles of light around traditional table and standard lamp shades create warm focal points. Strategically positioned, they provide adequate general light.

diffuses light to the sides. Thus both the material and the shape of the shade influence the light produced. A pale-coloured shade will diffuse more than a dark one, a smooth white or silver lining will reflect more light outwards, and a gold-varnished lining will produce an invitingly warm light. As for shape, a narrow cylindrical shade will cast a very limited beam in each direction, a wide-bottomed one will produce a broader spread below. Of the commoner shade types, the 'coolie' shade — narrow at the top, wide at the bottom like a Chinese hat — perhaps produces the most efficient and least glaring general light. For more specific control it is possible to buy shades that are completely closed at the top, directing all their light downwards — an effect that can also be achieved by the use of a crown-silvered bulb.

Portable lamps offer the great advantage that they can simply be plugged in and moved at will. But wherever they are placed, whether permanently or temporarily, care should be taken to ensure that they are positioned where they will not impede circulation and that the flex is safely kept out of the way — and not just under a loose rug, which can be very dangerous. For these reasons they usually have to be kept close to power points and to the sides of the room.

Pendants and wall brackets

The utilitarian pendant, despite its flat, unforgiving light, is still a feature of many contemporary interiors, often where resources, rental agreements or a short-term stay make installation of other types of fitting impractical or impossible. As with table lamps, however, the final lighting effect can be somewhat modified by the choice of shade. A small, open, cylindrical shade produces a very raw light which can be glaring from directly underneath; a better result can be achieved by the use of a wider shade, particularly a conical one, upturned to reflect most of its light back on to the ceiling. Much softer light is produced by hemispheres or globes of opal glass or plastic, and by the ubiquitous Japanese lanterns of translucent paper, popular today because they are cheap, simple and easy to replace.

More ornamental are chandeliers and traditional wall brackets. Deriving from the candle and gas fittings of the past, chandeliers and wall brackets impart a period, formal feel to an interior. When they are used for general light, however, their bright, uncontrolled output fails to imitate the soft, period atmosphere that was once produced by flickering candles and gas lamps. This should be borne in mind when selecting chandeliers and multiple-light wall sconces, particularly if the fittings use bare candle-bulbs or small, partial shades.

Various versions of candle-bulb exist, their size usually increasing with the wattage. Common types are 25, 40 or 60 watts with clear, frosted or fluted glass envelopes. To avoid glare, the lower wattages are recommended; this may mean, however, that some additional form of general lighting is needed. Another solution is to dim the fixtures in question, although this will inevitably result in losing some of the sparkle generated by a brightly burning bulb. If glare is to be totally avoided and sparkle still retained, the best solution for a chandelier would be to use highly dimmed bulbs within the chandelier itself and illuminate the glass from a distance with discreet low-voltage sources.

When installing a large chandelier, it goes without saying that you should ensure that the chain or cord is strong enough to bear the weight, and is firmly secured to a ceiling joist. Wall sconces, like other wall-mounted fittings, should usually be positioned about two-thirds up the height of the wall, no less than 2m/6½ft from the floor to prevent eye-level glare.

Left. A pair of stylistically simple pendants made for the low-voltage multi-mirror bulb. Here the bulb itself provides control, casting a bright beam on to objects directly below. The pink back-spill of light produced by the multi-mirror bulbs is caught in the glass of the shades, creating an attractive sparkle. Below. A futuristic metal-framed wall light available in different versions for tungsten or compact fluorescent bulbs. It uses translucent frosted glass as a diffusing screen.

Above. This living room is predominantly lit by the arrays of small recessed downlighters, discreetly set towards the edges of the ceiling. The pair of table lamps and the dimmed chandelier are purely ornamental. To achieve this effect, it is necessary to install each type of fitting on a separate circuit.

Combining the traditional with the modern

Many interiors demand the presence of traditional fixtures as part of a period style. However, it is possible to combine them successfully with other forms of general lighting, or simply with accent sources, to create a lively modern effect, taking the best from both worlds.

The most radical method is to introduce another source of general light such as a downlighter or wall-washer system, and keep the number of traditional sources to a minimum. Table lamps can then be introduced for task rather than general illumination.

If you prefer to use more than just one or two traditional fittings, it is possible to provide an alternative main system of general light on one switch circuit, and keep table lamps, chandelier or wall brackets on a separate circuit. In this way you could, for example, retain a central chandelier within the scheme, but keep its output to a glow while illuminating the walls more strongly with wall-washers. If a dimmer is provided on each circuit, this method allows you to make adjustments in emphasis.

An electrical contractor can provide a separate circuit for two- and five-amp wall sockets for table and standard lamps. A dimmer in this circuit will make it possible to dim all the portable lamps in the room from one central point. Since the sockets differ from standard 13-amp outlets there is no danger of accidental connection of a vacuum cleaner or other appliance, which would damage the dimmer. In a large room with chandelier and table lamps plus downlighters, wall-washers or uplighters it is advisable to allocate separate circuits to each type of illumination; in smaller areas two-amp outlets for table lamps could well be linked in the same circuit as chandelier and wall brackets.

It is often worth considering the use of downlighters to light the dark centre of a room that is lit by table lamps around the sides, fulfilling the traditional role of the pendant. In a room 3m/10ft square, which could be well illuminated solely by an array of five downlighters, the correct combination might be two or three table lamps and two downlighters. Although the resulting effect is less even than pure downlighting, the table lamps are usefully incorporated into the scheme. Again, separate circuits and dimmers can be used to control the balance between the two types of source.

DOWNLIGHTING

General lighting by downlighters can give an intimate atmosphere to a living room. The focus is moved to a lower, more comfortable level. Emphasis is placed on the objects in the room rather than on its shape, with pools of light cast on to table-tops and on to the textured and coloured surfaces of carpets and upholstery. Contrasts can be created by adding accent sources to cast light upwards or highlight special features.

Downlighter fittings, whether surface-mounted, fully or semi-recessed, are most at home in plain or modern ceilings. If used unsympathetically they can look incongruous in a period ceiling with fibrous-plaster ceiling-rose and mouldings, and it shows little regard for conservation to drill holes into a very fine ceiling in order to recess the fittings. Among the tremendous range now available, however, there are many fittings which are extremely small, such as the newer low-voltage types, which can be inserted very discreetly into an ornate ceiling.

When choosing a downlighter, it is important to consider both the wattage required for the

Above. Even general lighting, produced by a symmetrical array of fully recessed downlighters, blends well with the soothing beige and grey decor of this room. The downward light also shimmers on the shiny surface of the coffee table and sparkles on glass and crystal ornaments. At the end of the room, a pair of china table lamps cast small, bright pools of light, which simply serve to create a warmer atmosphere. Additional accent is provided by spot-lights either side of the shelf unit.

room (see p14) and the size of ceiling aperture required by the fitting. Generally, the more powerful the bulb, the larger the aperture. Since intensity falls off over a distance, higher ceilings demand more powerful bulbs. Avoid using fittings with very large apertures in low ceilings — they can often seem like craters when so close to the eye.

For a pure downlighting effect, it is wise to keep an array of downlighters in the central section of the ceiling. If placed closer to the walls, downlighters may produce arcs or scallops of light across the wall surface, an effect which can be interesting but is not always desirable. When planning an array for the living room it is important to consider the positions of the main items of furniture and mark them on to a sketch of the lighting plan. Avoid placing downlighters immediately above a chair or sofa, since the direct downward output would be unflattering to someone seated below. Instead, arrange for the downlighters to be positioned to the side of, slightly forward of, or back from seating, and add a task light if necessary to ensure comfortable reading.

Where downlighters are used for general lighting, additional downlighters, but separately switched, can be added to the ceiling array as accent lights, giving a satisfying overall unity to the lighting scheme. Alternatively, interesting contrasts can be achieved by using other types of source for accent; perhaps an uplighter throwing a shaft of light on to the ceiling , which is dim except for the bright circles of the downlighter fittings themselves, or a directional fitting, casting a beam diagonally on to a wall.

To achieve downlight in a room with a sloping ceiling, a directional downlighter will usually be needed, angled to keep the output straight downwards. It is possible to buy fully recessed downlighters for this purpose, although their average depth is approximately 20cm/8in. If sufficient recess space is not available, semi-recessed or eyeball fittings could be used.

Below. An array of unobtrusive, recessed downlighters emphasizes the uncluttered nature of this room, and the cool light from their silver reflectors accentuates the white carpet and walls and the chrome frames of the chairs. Contrasting upward shafts of light, which make a feature of the slanting walls, are produced by drum uplighters in the corners.

Obviously, the most efficient place to position an uplighter is in the centre of the room. This is often the practice in spacious public areas such as banking halls, hotel lobbies and large offices, where people can easily circulate around the fittings. The more cramped furniture layout of most domestic living rooms, however, often means that uplighters must be positioned on or close to a wall, or possibly in a corner. When they are used in this way, the bright beam from tungsten-halogen uplighters may be sharply cut

Left. This entrance is given dramatic emphasis by uplighting, a theme to be continued in the adjoining living area (shown opposite). The effect is achieved by using a continuous series of fluorescent tubes set within the enlarged cornice. Wall sconces with candle bulbs give a contrastingly warm and old-fashioned touch. Below. Uplighting can be produced more simply with these sleek, portable fittings, which can be fitted with 200, 300 or 500 watt tungsten-halogen bulbs.

UPLIGHTING

If you prefer to create a sense of height, or if the ceiling has fine plasterwork worth making a feature of, then uplighters are the answer for general lighting. They also offer the easiest way of achieving a modern lighting effect in a period setting. No work need be done on the ceiling and the uplighters themselves are available in designs that fit well with period styles. Some reproduce or follow designs of the 1920s and 1930s, some imitate period shapes, while others — in particular those made for the tungsten-halogen bulb — have more modern, yet classically simple forms that work well with traditional furnishings.

When considering the use of uplighters for general lighting, always bear in mind that they use the ceiling as a reflector to bounce light back down into the room. Uplighting a pale-coloured ceiling will produce a light and airy effect, whereas illumination from a dark-coloured surface will be considerably less. Remember also that glossy or mirrored ceiling surfaces may reflect an image of the bulb itself.

Of the many types of uplighter suitable for the living room, those using mains-voltage tungsten-halogen bulbs are by far the most efficient. Only one or two fittings are necessary for an average-sized room. Given the highly sculptural form of these fittings, however, many interiors use two as a pair, even though only one may be necessary in lighting terms. This does not present a problem since bulbs exist in wattages ranging from 200 to 500 so the light intensity can be adjusted as necessary.

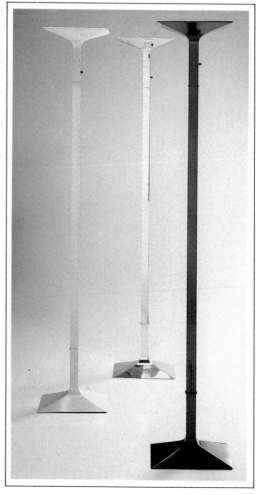

Above. Light from two pairs of large, mains-voltage, tungsten-halogen uplighters — positioned above the pillars — exploits the full architectural potential of the barrelled ceiling which, being pale in colour, reflects light back into this stately room. The bright, whitish light is typical of a halogen bulb. Low-voltage, narrow-beam sources set into radiator casings under the window accent the curves of the window arch. Two floor lights provide task lighting at a more intimate level.

off, producing a noticeable line across the wall at the level where the light is emitted. Thus, if an uplighter is positioned too close to a painting, the beam can cut unattractively across it. Little can be done to reduce this effect. Instead, the best solution is to place the uplighter in front of a window or a bare wall where the shape produced by the light becomes a feature in itself.

Softer effects may be achieved with uplighters that use GLS or standard tungsten reflector bulbs. In the living room, one or two small drum uplighters concealed behind furniture or beneath plants can provide excellent supplementary general lighting. In particular, one positioned beneath or beside the television will provide adequate and reflection-free background lighting for television-watching. These and other GLS-bulb uplighters can be used as a means of general lighting. However, at least four or even six are needed for an average-sized living room, and it is advisable to keep the space light in colour and sparsely furnished so as to allow as much light as possible to be reflected throughout the room.

WALL-WASHING

Not all rooms and furniture layouts permit the use of wall-washing as a method of general lighting. The number of fittings required to give a sufficiently high level of illumination is roughly equivalent to the number of table lamps of identical wattage needed to do the same job. The number will depend on variables such as the colour of the walls, carpets and furniture as well as the size of the room. But while table lamps can be placed almost anywhere, wall-washers can only be positioned at regular intervals, a set distance from the wall (see instructions on positioning, p17). Wall-washers therefore require a suitable length of uninterrupted wall, where they can be positioned without problems of glare.

Furthermore, although three or four wall-washers along a single wall may be enough to light a room 3m/10ft square, the reflected light would not reach across a room 4.5-6m/15-20ft deep. In such a case it would be necessary to wall-wash the wall opposite as well, or to add another form of general lighting on the other side of the room. A suitable addition might be matching downlighters made with the same aperture as the wall-washers so that they have a consistent appearance in the ceiling. This combination could be particularly effective in a room where one entire wall is covered in prints. Wall-washers directed at the wall would highlight the prints — a dramatic effect if the wall is dark in colour — and downlighters would provide more general light.

Left. A classic wall-wash effect, used on bare walls, increases the sense of spaciousness in this elegant city apartment. The warm light from gold reflectors softens the stark contrast of the colour scheme. Above and right. In a carefully considered scheme, light from wide-beam, low-voltage, recessed sources grazes the walls, bringing out the coarse texture of the wall covering as well as lighting calligraphy and hangings. A drum uplighter at the foot of the window, a narrow-beam source above the chimney breast, and the fire itself, provide further accent.

A successful scheme in a traditional setting is often to wall-wash the alcoves either side of a fireplace. This provides excellent illumination for book-shelves and displays, leaving the mantel-piece and chimney breast in the centre to be lit by a more specific accent source. Again, another form of general lighting is necessary to supplement the wall-washers.

Above. Soft background light emanates from drum uplighters, positioned beneath plants to throw leafy shadows on to the ceiling. Contrastingly bright accents are provided by a framing projector on the picture, a narrow-beam, low-voltage source on the flowers, and strip-lamps in the alcove. Apart from a task light on the desk, all sources are carefully concealed.

ACCENT LIGHTING

While general lighting sets the scene, accent sources introduce drama and contrast. Their function is primarily aesthetic rather than practical: to distinguish and balance different areas of the room, highlight centres of activity such as coffee or dining tables, and bring out pictures, plants and other decorative objects. Occasionally accent fittings are the main source of light in a room, for example, spotlights with wide, directional beams.

Accent lighting can be produced by many different fittings; which one will depend on exactly what is to be featured. As a rule, it is wise to keep the fittings as discreet as possible: attention should be drawn to the object or space being accented, not to the source of light.

For accent lighting to be effective it should be clearly defined and controlled separately from the surrounding general illumination. This also makes it possible to create a series of different effects and atmospheres by using dimmers to vary the balance of general and accent lighting (see pp82–87).

A word of caution however. With the development of ever more sophisticated and precise fittings in recent years, the field of accent lighting invites all types of experiment. It is important to remember that if too many different effects are used in one area, the result can look over-lit, and the contrast necessary for accent can be lost altogether. Decide first of all what the main features of the space really are, and be selective in the choice of subjects for highlighting.

Above. A variety of accent sources emphasize the main features of this conventional room plan. Tungsten strip-lamps, set behind a small pelmet, give low-level interest to shelving either side of the fireplace, also providing light for a drinks tray. Recessed wall-washers brightly illuminate bookshelves and a recessed framing projector throws a tight rectangle of light on to the picture.

Accenting furniture and features

The simplest forms of accenting can be achieved by almost any type of light source. Consider for example a small living room with general lighting provided by four downlighters. The addition of a fifth downlighter or eyeball fitting directing light on to a central coffee table can provide a well-defined focal point, so long as the light falling here is stronger than the general illumination. The difference in intensity could be generated simply with different bulb wattages or by dimming the surrounding general light sources.

In this case, the beam of the accent downlighter should be confined as far as possible to the surface of the table. If, however, the intention is to highlight a plant or vase of flowers on the table the beam should be even more tightly controlled. This effect could be created by using, say, a PAR 38 spot with a beam angle of 17° or a low-voltage source with a beam angle of only 10°.

Another simple form of accent lighting is to illuminate an alcove containing shelving or some other form of display. Here there may be no need for special reflectors since, if the alcoves are sufficiently deep, the two sides will be all that is needed to keep the light contained. Tungsten strip-lamps, concealed behind mouldings or shelf fitments, are one possibility. Wall-washing an alcove is also effective, and, if the alcove has glass shelves, a single downlighter placed at top centre is an easy solution.

Accenting plants

Plants and flower arrangements are perfect subjects for accent. Specific light will bring out the texture as well as the colour of leaves and blooms, and can accentuate the form of the plant or arrangement, often casting striking shadows. It can also stimulate plant growth.

Most plants need between 12 and 16 hours of light a day, though the intensity of the light required will vary according to the natural habitat of the plant. As a general rule, foliage plants such as ferns, miniature palms and aspidistras need much less light than cacti, succulents and blooming plants such as African violets, orchids, citruses and yuccas. Deprived of adequate light, a plant may survive but fail to produce new leaves and flowers, and the stems may grow thin and lanky. An accent light can thus make both decorative and gardening sense.

Any type of bulb can be used; tungsten sources with their mellow colour rendering are sympathetic to blowzy arrangements of summer flowers, whereas tungsten-halogen bulbs produce a whiter, more Mediterranean feel. The ideal light for plant growth has a mixture of red, infra-red and blue rays which can be provided either by placing two 40-watt fluorescent tubes, one 'cool white', one 'daylight' in tone, side by side, or by using specialist tubes such as Grolux

Above. The shiny green leaves and creamy white and pink blooms of this orchid are highlighted by a low-voltage, narrow-beam, ceiling-mounted spotlight above it (unseen). Such lighting makes the single, luxuriant plant a dramatic element in this sumptuous room. An adjustable brass lamp mounted on the wall lights the sofa.

tubes. These are available in a range from 15 to 65 watts, and can be installed into standard fluorescent fittings. Grolux tubes would be enough to grow plants in the complete absence of natural light, however their mauve-coloured output and the lack of beam control restrict their decorative use. Tungsten-halogen fittings offer far more scope in terms of effect.

Small plants and flower arrangements on table tops are best lit by sources on the ceiling, particularly by narrow-beam spots. Larger plants and indoor trees standing on the floor might be lit from below by drum uplighters so that they cast leafy shadows on the ceiling. This would be particularly dramatic in combination with general downlighting since the shadows would stand out against the dimmer ceiling.

Tungsten and tungsten-halogen sources produce far more heat than fluorescents, so particular care should be taken in positioning. If the bulb is too close, the leaves will curl and become scorched. Check for this by feeling the

temperature of the leaves closest to the light source: if they are warm, move the source further away. If this is not convenient, consider using a lower wattage or special cool-beam source such as a dichroic multi-mirror bulb (see p25).

Above. A narrow-beam recessed downlighter gives a pretty sparkle to this plant display, accentuating the different forms, colours and textures of leaves and flowers. Besides its visual benefits, the light also encourages rapid growth.

Accenting pictures and sculpture

The living room is usually the site of the best pictures in the house, and where they are contemplated for longest. It is worth taking trouble to light them well. This area is where purpose-designed and low-voltage accent sources come into their own. Whereas a conventional brass picture light attached to the top of the frame produces a bright patch high on the picture and casts less light below, a well chosen spotlight, properly used, can provide even illumination over the whole picture. Fittings should be selected according to the beam angle required. (To estimate this see p23.)

The successful lighting of a large picture can often best be achieved by 'cross-lighting', using two spotlights close to, and either side of the picture so that their outputs cross on the surface. This is a particularly good solution for pictures and hangings which are unusually wide and shallow. It can also bring out texture as the light will graze the surface at an angle.

Above. Simple, track-mounted fittings with wide beams accent objects of interest and also give good general light within a large space. However, bulky fittings like these need a high ceiling to be successful.

Reflections are often a problem in lighting glass-covered pictures and heavily varnished oil paintings. Where glass is present in the frame, the problem can be minimized by the use of special non-reflective glass. For oil paintings it is a good idea to first test for reflection by wiring up a spotlight on a long lead and checking out the various positions. Reflection will occur more at some angles than at others. If there is no point which is completely free of reflection, consider then the angle from which the picture is most often viewed and light it so that it appears most satisfactorily from that point. Also try hanging the picture tilted slightly away from the wall.

Where valuable or delicate pictures and textiles are concerned, conservation factors should also be taken into account. In museums and art galleries where pictures are lit constantly through the day, the maximum light level for oil paintings is often limited to 150 lux, that for watercolours and textiles to only 50 lux. In the home, levels are far less critical as pictures will not be lit for such extended periods — in fact by far the greatest danger is direct sunlight. The lux level expected from a fitting at a defined distance is usually given in the manufacturers' specifications; individual bulb specifications are provided for fittings that take reflector bulbs.

The heat generated by an accent source may also be a matter for concern. Generally, the heat generated by a bulb is relative to its wattage; thus, low-voltage sources, which are often two or three times lower in wattage than their mains-voltage equivalents, produce a cooler output. Cooler still are dichroic bulbs such as the cool-beam PAR 38 and the multi-mirrors. Care should be taken in installation of dichroic bulbs so that the fittings have suitable ventilation at the rear.

The most sophisticated and dramatic form of accent lighting is produced by the framing projector, a low-voltage fitting that includes a system of shutters and lenses which enable the light beam to be exactly shaped to the size of the picture it is accenting. The resulting effect is extremely even and because there is no stray light the picture appears to be lit from behind. Specialists can also cut metal masks to fit inside these projectors so that a sculpture or abstract shape can be perfectly framed by the beam. Framing projectors are available as surface, track and recessed fittings. Considerable care should be taken in their positioning to achieve the correct beam coverage — some manufacturers provide a table for their fittings indicating exactly what size of picture can be illuminated from varying distances.

Similar in principle to picture lighting, the accenting of three-dimensional objects such as sculpture requires special attention to the direction of the light. Interesting effects — or sometimes odd distortions — can result from lighting the object from behind or from an acute angle. Cross-lighting can often prove a useful technique, particularly if the piece is to be viewed from more than one angle.

Below. This neat pair of miniature, low-voltage uplighters — called 'Highlights' — offer the accent capability of a spotlight without the need for any special wiring. The fittings are completely portable, having built-in transformers. Different beam angles can be achieved simply by changing the bulb, which can be tilted to different positions within the fitting. Bottom. Fitted with a wide-beam bulb, the 'Highlight' casts light right across a large canvas (left). With a narrow-beam bulb, it dramatically pinpoints a sculpture (right).

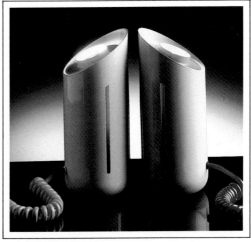

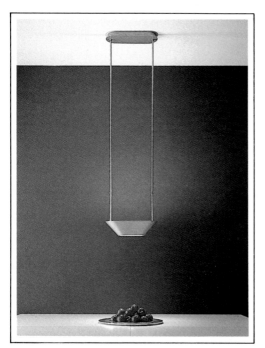

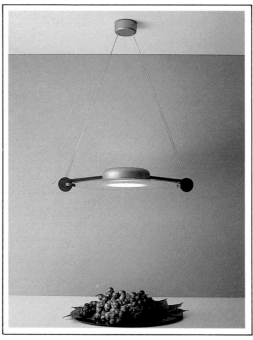

Above. Ideal for lighting a dining table are these two modern Italian pendants. One (left) has two separate sources for uplighting and downlighting, the other (right) gives downlight alone. Both are low-voltage.

The atmosphere created by the lighting in a dining room is very important. Ideally it should be flattering both to the faces of the diners and the food before them, conducive to pleasure and conversation. Yet often it has to cover a variety of different social functions; for example, the general lighting for a children's tea party will need to be much higher than for a formal dinner party or just a friendly supper. It is therefore important to begin planning a scheme by carefully assessing the different types of ambience required.

The traditional pattern has been to hang a central chandelier or pendant high above the table and supplement this with wall brackets and possibly picture lights. As we have seen before, however, widespread uncontrolled sources such as a chandelier provide very flat overall light and offer little variation. Much can be done to improve the atmosphere of the space by using more carefully controlled sources. If the decor dictates that traditional fittings are present, the effect can be softened simply by installing dimmers. If possible, two circuits should be used; one for the pendant and one for wall brackets and picture lights.

Whatever the style, the dining table will inevitably be the centrepiece and there are a variety of ways to provide illumination for it. One possibility is a low pendant, which can look most attractive from a distance but can become an obstacle if it hangs between two people seated opposite each other. A fitting with a rise-and-fall mechanism can be a solution, since it can be adjusted to suit the moment. However, a much more effective means of bringing light down over the table is the use of downlighters.

To produce an intimate atmosphere for a dinner party, a single downlighter using a PAR 38 or ISL bulb is quite sufficient over an average-sized table, around 125cm/4ft square. For family meals, a greater level of illumination will be required. This could be catered for by allowing for a higher level of general illumination elsewhere in the scheme, or increasing the number of downlighters above the table. Common configurations for an array are four downlighters above a large square table, say 1.5–2m/5–6½ft square, or a row of three or four downlighters over a long refectory table. (The exact number of fittings required can be calculated as described on p14.) Remember that the distance involved in this instance, however, is that from the ceiling to the table surface, rather than to the floor.

For a more dramatic setting, low-voltage downlighters with narrow beams can provide very striking effects, particularly if focused on to a central display of fruit or flowers. A narrow shaft of light falling in the centre also tends to draw the guests seated around the table together. The intimacy of this effect can be further enhanced with candles. Nevertheless this type of lighting, like candles alone, cannot provide sufficient general light for the room.

Above. A trio of low-slung pendants provide glare-free light over a large oval table and give a sparkle to glass and silverware. Additional general light comes from the row of recessed downlighters in the window alcove. The light level is kept low to make the most of the dramatic night-time view from this high-rise dining room. Right. Narrow, low-voltage beams from an array of four downlighters bring out the warm colour and beautiful grain of a wooden refectory table. Candlesticks affirm the traditional theme. The single drum uplighter in the corner gives supplementary general light for circulation, and two small, directional low-voltage sources give a glow to the richly coloured hangings.

Wall lights or a widely spread array of downlighters are needed to provide overall illumination for circulation, seating and serving.

Pictures are often an important element in the dining room and the lighting for them should be arranged on a separate circuit from table and general lighting. A framing projector on one special picture is particularly effective in combination with the low-voltage table centre effect described above. Additional low-voltage or narrow-beam mains-voltage sources positioned directly over consoles and sideboards are also both dramatic and practical.

A study is by definition a work space. The priority is thus to ensure that adequate illumination is provided for reading and writing. Mood lighting is secondary, though many of us feel we can work more easily in certain types of atmosphere, be it bright and spaciously modern or sombre as a Victorian library.

Practical illumination for a study can be provided in one of two ways. Either the entire space is lit to a very high level, with halogen uplighters or an array of powerful downlighters, or the general lighting may be kept to a lower level, similar to that for a living room, and a number of task lights used in addition. The second solution is generally more cost effective, particularly in terms of running costs.

Even in situations where a task light alone seems sufficient for the job in hand, a low level of general illumination is necessary to prevent eye strain over an extended period of work. This is particularly important where a home computer and VDU screen are in use. Care should be taken in positioning and choosing the type of task light, to ensure that glare is not produced and that reflections are not created on the VDU screen. For the same reason, general lighting should ideally be indirect; uplighting or wall-washing would be equally suitable.

Left. Though furnished along traditional lines, this study unobtrusively uses very up-to-date lighting: two low-voltage, recessed accent sources clearly illuminate the group of paintings, while an adjustable low-voltage task light on the desk provides good light for reading and writing. Right. In this cosy, old-fashioned study-cum-sitting-room, perhaps designed more as a peaceful refuge than as a place for serious work, most of the illumination is provided by a large table lamp, its mellow tungsten output bringing out the vivid colours of tulips and poinsettias, and of the paisley-pattern upholstery. The clouded glass of a large antique mirror behind the lamp reflects light back into the room, increasing the overall illumination. A recessed, low-voltage, directional downlighter accentuates the rich sheen and warm colour of the dappled walls.

A basic scheme for an average-sized study, (around 3m/10ft square) is to use a single freestanding halogen uplighter with a 300 or 500 watt bulb, plus one or two task lights. If fitted with a dimmer, the uplighter can provide strong overall illumination for daytime activities on overcast days, and a softer glow for late-night reading. In a room where books are dominant, with an expanse of bookshelves across one wall, a more appropriate effect could be wall-washing, again supplemented with task lights.

The choice of desk light often depends on the surface space available as well as the requirements of the user. A traditional table lamp can provide enough light for reading and writing, and gives the room a relaxed, domestic feel. Adjustable task lights such as the classic Anglepoise allow far more variation in function and provide a more directed beam for precise work. More efficient light still is produced by a new generation of adjustable task lights using the compact fluorescent sources such as the Thorn 2D, PL or miniature double-ended fluorescent bulbs. There are a variety of options if desk space is limited, many models being available in clamp, screw-down, wall-bracket and floor-standing versions as well as with a conventional weighted base for the table top.

Task lights for writing should be positioned so as to avoid both glare and shadow. The ideal position is a little to the left of a right-handed writer and the reverse for a left-handed person. This is to ensure that the hand does not cast a shadow on the page. The general lighting should also be arranged to cast light evenly over the entire working surface. The same principles also apply to natural light. Thus, a desk should not be placed immediately in front of or under a window where sunlight will stream in on fine days, possibly producing too much glare. The most effective general lighting for work on a bright clear day would be the indirect light from a north-facing window.

Below. The large-scale Anglepoise used inventively as both uplighter and downlighter. One fitting here is pointed upwards to bounce general light off the ceiling. The other is directed more conventionally over the desk top.

The lighting needs of a studio, home office or other work-room are similar in principle to those of a study. However, the work for which they are used, from drawing and painting to needlework or carpentry, often requires a higher level of overall illumination.

Halogen uplighters can be ideal, provided that the ceiling is over 2.5m/8ft high. Should this not be so, even light distribution will be difficult to achieve from uplighters. The table opposite gives approximate numbers of uplighters required in different sized spaces; the intensity of the light produced can be adjusted by using different wattage bulbs. Where the ceiling is too low for uplighting, ceiling-mounted halogen wall-washers could provide a similar degree of indirect light but with a vertical emphasis.

Ceiling-mounted fluorescent sources would also be effective, and less expensive to run. Fluorescent battens now exist in many attractive casings, and most are fitted with carefully designed anti-glare louvres or diffusers. Many European manufacturers are also marketing tubular systems for fluorescent sources which can be suspended or fixed directly to the wall or ceiling or arranged in rectangles and other configurations. Particularly effective is a suspended system with the fluorescent sources pointing directly upwards at the ceiling. In this way the lighting effect becomes indirect, and all possibility of glare is removed.

Above. The ubiquitous Anglepoise makes an excellent studio task light. Opposite. An office receives overall illumination at a level and tone similar to bright daylight from wall-mounted tungsten-halogen uplighters. A low ceiling means that a number of fittings have to be used around the walls, and has made 'hot spots' — bright patches on the ceiling — inevitable. Below. A suspended fluorescent fitting with wide 'gull-wing' reflectors gives an efficient and very economical light for working — a fluorescent tube uses up to five times less electricity than a tungsten bulb.

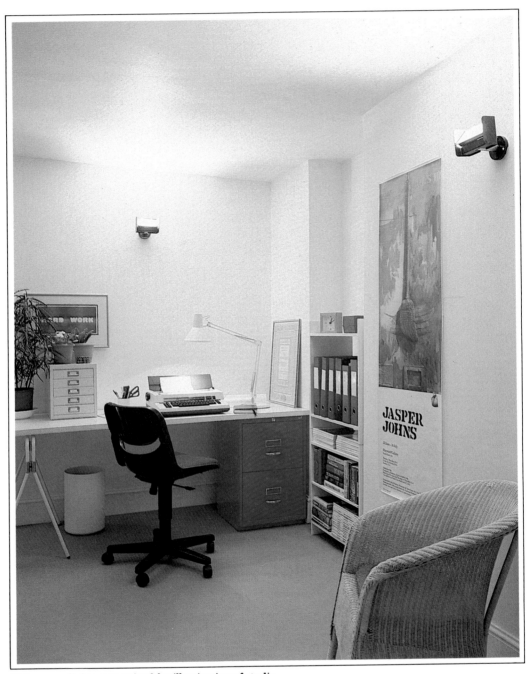

Halogen uplighters required for illumination of studio

Dimensions of room	Ceiling height		
	2·5m/8ft (no less)	2·5–3m/8–10ft	3–4m/10–13ft
2·5 × 3m/8 × 10ft	1 × 500 watt	1 × 500 watt	1 × 500 watt
3·5 × 4·5m/12 × 14ft	2 × 300 watt	2 × 300 or 500 watt	2 × 500 watt
5 × 6m/16 × 20ft	4 × 300 watt	4 × 300 or 500 watt	4 × 500 watt

The kitchen today is the most important room in many homes. In the past, when most middle-class households included servants, kitchen design was often disregarded. Now, most people cook for themselves, whether they regard it as a pleasure or a chore, creating a demand for an attractive and efficient working environment. At the same time, a more relaxed and informal way of life has encouraged a trend towards eating in the kitchen, which thereby becomes an all-purpose family room. Whether the kitchen in question is a high tech food laboratory or the nostalgic country pine centre of family life, its functional lighting needs will be the same.

GENERAL LIGHTING

The most important aspect to consider in a kitchen is the general lighting. It is this which will enable you to work easily and safely, and it is by this light that you will perform most activities, from cleaning to looking inside cupboards and reading low-level controls on kitchen machines. There are several effective options, all of which rely on broad beam distribution of light.

Track and spotlights

For practicality combined with ease of installation, a system of tracking and spotlights is an obvious choice, particularly for a small galley kitchen. In this case, a long length of track run down the centre of the ceiling and fitted with up to four or five spotlights can provide good illumination for sink, cupboards, cooker and working surfaces. Choose wide-beam spotlights, as the dramatic shadows created by narrow beams are inappropriate in the kitchen, where even illumination is the prime consideration. The track and spot solution is attractive for its versatility; tracks are also relatively inexpensive to install.

When it comes to lighting a larger kitchen, however, problems can arise with the track and spot method. Although a central track is ideal in a long, thin galley kitchen, the same solution will produce bands of glare and shadow in a room more than 2m/6½ft wide. This can be resolved by using two parallel tracks, or even a rectangular tracking system, always ensuring that the track is positioned no more than 1m/3¼ft away from the edge of wall cupboards and work surfaces. In this way, light can fall directly on to

Left. A row of powerful spotlights provide bright and functional illumination in this simply designed kitchen. The creamy white ceiling, walls, units and work-tops have very high reflectance, and increase the effectiveness of the fittings. The resulting high level of general light in the room makes any specifically directed task lighting, over the cooker for example, unnecessary.

Right. General light produced by a series of fluorescent tubes. Their cold-toned light, and the reflections cast on to the glossy surfaces of ceiling and wall units, underline the slick 1960s style of the room. The fluorescent tubes have been fitted on battens along the tops of the wall units, with a neat acrylic cover added to conceal the fittings and effectively diffuse the light.

working surfaces without the user's body casting a shadow. In large kitchens, a greater number of lower wattage fittings will produce a more pleasant and even result than fewer high wattage fixtures.

A group of low-wattage spotlights is also the best answer for kitchens with low ceilings, where the fittings will be positioned close to people's heads. The heat produced by more powerful spotlights could cause discomfort.

Fluorescent sources

Fluorescent sources provide cool and very efficient general lighting; in some cases, their output is equivalent to that of tungsten bulbs almost five times the wattage. Fluorescents also tend to have a longer life than their tungsten or tungsten-halogen equivalents.

The output from a fluorescent tube is diffuse and much more difficult to control with reflectors than that from other bulbs. However its long, thin shape makes it capable of lighting a large area very evenly. This is an advantage in the kitchen, where good overall illumination is essential, although the effect often appears flat compared with the sculptured output from downlighters. A wide range of fluorescent tubes now exists, offering colourations varying from 'daylight' to 'warm white'. None approach the warm colour of tungsten light, so necessary for the mellow

atmosphere required, for example, by a country-style kitchen. But it is possible to select fluorescent fittings suitable for use as working lights only, with supplementary tungsten lighting for other activities such as dining.

One scheme which is highly successful in a kitchen where the ceiling is at least 80cm/31in higher than the top of the wall cupboards is to install fluorescent tubes running along the tops of the cupboards and conceal them with a simple wooden baffle. The effect is extremely pleasant, totally indirect uplighting.

The use of more conventional forms of uplighting in the kitchen is usually restricted, since it is common for all available wall space to be taken up with cupboards and appliances, making an even arrangement of wall-mounted fittings impossible, while floor-standing fittings are also impractical given the need for clear floor space. Ceiling-mounted uplighters suspended from the ceiling could be used if there is sufficient height. Both fluorescent and halogen types would be suitable for this application.

Whatever fluorescent sources you wish to use, remember that it is difficult to dim them without very special control gear and wiring. If an additional, more subtle lighting scheme will be called for at various times, a quite different source, separately switched, will be required.

Downlighters

Downlighters, though more expensive and complicated to install, are often in the long run a neat solution to a kitchen's needs. A decorative advantage is the discreet and timeless appearance of a downlighter, which can fit unobtrusively into any style of kitchen. A practical advantage is that a downlighter, whether fully recessed or semi-recessed into the ceiling, gathers little dirt; track and spots on the other hand accumulate a lot of dirt and grease in a kitchen and are often awkward to clean. In respect of the lighting effect, a downlighter usually offers greater glare control. Place a spot in the wrong position or bounce its light at an awkward angle and the

Above. A warm working light is given by recessed downlighters with gold reflectors, fitted with 100-watt bulbs. Concealed strip-lights illuminate the work surface.

glare can be intolerable. The grooved, black inner casing and baffles or reflectors of a well-designed downlighter will prevent this.

Similar neatness of appearance is offered by eyeball fittings. These have the added advantage for kitchens that they can be angled to light surfaces that lie directly beneath wall units and shelves, surfaces which the output of an ordinary downlighter would not reach. For this purpose eyeballs should be installed in the ceiling about 80-100cm/31-39in back from the surface to be lit.

DINING AREAS

Few people nowadays use a totally separate dining room for every meal. A medium-sized kitchen will probably have a table in the centre or against one wall, and the lighting scheme should accentuate this separate function. It should aim to create two entirely different atmospheres within the same space.

The problem is similar, on a smaller scale, to that of many restaurants: that is, how to provide enough lighting over the table so that the diners can see what they are eating, but to define and restrict the light sufficiently to make them unaware of the other tables and people in the room. Each table must have its own focus. So in

Above. Low-voltage recessed downlighters with wide-beam multi-mirror bulbs provide glare-free light for dining and enrich the varnished pine table top. Similar fittings with narrow-beam bulbs highlight the plants.

the domestic kitchen the dining table should have an independent light source separately controlled from the rest of the lighting. Obvious solutions are a pendant fitting, individual spot or single downlighter producing a pool of light that encompasses only the centre of the table—the narrow spread of illumination is necessary to prevent unpleasant downward shadows falling on the diners' faces. If general lighting is then set at a low level, an attractive emphasis is given to the table but ample light still exists for serving.

TASK LIGHTING

There are three main areas in any kitchen which may require task lighting: the cooker, the sink and the working surface, whether this is a counter beneath wall units or a separate piece of furniture in the centre of the room. Many kitchens will need further specific lighting depending on their design and use.

In a small galley kitchen lit by track and spots there may well be no need for additional task lighting. If the spots are carefully positioned and angled on to working surfaces, these general light fittings alone will serve. A larger kitchen, however, is likely to need more careful attention. Where a ceiling array is planned, a simple solution is to add an extra downlighter or spotlight above the sink, cooker or work surface. Another possibility is to suspend a row of pendants hung low and close together over a counter or work surface to provide a bright, even light. Task lighting for the cooker is often made unnecessary by the fact that many modern cookers have their own task lights set under an eye-level grill, and that most separate cooker hoods also offer this facility.

Above. Efficient and attractive lighting for a small, workmanlike kitchen is produced by a series of simple, metal-shaded pendants hung directly above cooker, sink and work-tops.

The back of work-tops beneath wall-cupboards also needs to be well lit. Some kitchen units come with strip-lighting already fitted and concealed by a wood or laminate pelmet. If your units are specially designed and built, or if your ready-made ones come without this feature, then some form of lighting for this dim space should be considered an essential addition. There are two main types of strip-lighting for this purpose: the old-fashioned tungsten strip-lamp and the new, slimmer fluorescent tube. While tungsten sources offer a warmer, more mellow output, their elongated filament is extremely fragile, particularly when hot. This can be a distinct disadvantage since the filament is vulnerable to the vibrations caused by closing of cupboard doors above. Fluorescent tubes do not suffer from this problem and generally have a longer life. They also have a lower heat output which may prevent damage to any perishables stored in the cupboard immediately above them.

Above. A large store cupboard, crammed with kitchen products, is lit from within by a tungsten strip-lamp fitted vertically just to the right of the door opening.

Deep cupboards, larders and dim but useful corners may also need special attention. An extra spotlight or strip-lamp can make these much more practical areas to use. For cupboards, an internal strip-lamp could be installed on a simple door-operated switch.

It is useful to have task lighting connected to a different switch from general lighting. Besides saving energy, this makes it possible to obscure dirty pots and pans and other kitchen debris from view while you sit down to eat under general light.

Right. A fluorescent tube fitted beneath wall units gives bright, low-level task lighting. General light is provided by unusual fittings which consist of a bare low-voltage tungsten-halogen bulb suspended from the ceiling. The light is reflected off the ceiling, creating an effect similar to uplighting. The cold tones of halogen and fluorescent light are appropriate in this starkly modern scheme.

Above. Subtle accent lighting in the form of low-voltage pin-spot downlighters, set between the curtains and blinds, can be used independently of the more general illumination from recessed downlighters, whose gold reflectors bring out the warm beige tones of the furnishings.

The bedroom is usually simpler in function and furnishings than the living room, yet has just as much need for subtlety of atmosphere. The lighting plan could follow the same pattern as for a living room, that is with a good source of general light, separate task lights and an overlay of accent sources. This will often be necessary if the room contains a writing desk or sofa and is expected to double as an occasional study or sitting room. But if it is to be used exclusively as a bedroom, it could have a simpler scheme that combines general and task or general and accent functions.

Any form of general lighting used in the living room may be applied in the bedroom, although the overall level of illumination here rarely need be as high. You therefore probably need fewer or lower wattage fittings for general lighting: the maximum number of sources in an average 3m/10ft square bedroom being four downlighters or one halogen uplighter. The colour scheme of course affects lighting requirements. If the walls and floor are a dark colour, you need approximately one and a half times the intensity of light needed in a pale-coloured room — a basic property of light being that it is absorbed by dark colours but reflected by pale ones.

Wide-beam sources of general light give the bedroom an appropriately soft, all-embracing light. If downlighters are chosen to provide this, remember not to position them directly above the bedheads as the glare can be extremely disturbing when you lie down. For this reason uplighters are often preferable.

Since there is less need for overall illumination, an attractive as well as economical approach is to combine general and accent lighting in one source. Instead of using the down-lighters as an array, you could position them as accent lights above a plant, low chest or occasional table. They will still provide adequate general light. If you position a downlighter very close to the wall, light will fall in a scallop-shape down the wall and spill over on to the floor, sufficient both to illuminate a picture and to provide general lighting reflected from both wall and floor.

For a more theatrical look, you could take this technique even further by using narrow-beam, low-voltage sources within a dark colour scheme. The narrow beams make objects such as sculpture, a vase, plant or painting into dramatic focal points, with overspill of general light reduced almost to zero, creating a sophisticated and seductive atmosphere.

Above right. A lighting scheme is brought to life by the contrast created by a row of low-voltage eyeball downlighters set into the window recess. The bright scallops of light from their wide-beam reflector bulbs lessen the weight of the dark curtains. A simple, traditional table lamp provides light at the bedside. Right. A bed, lit by fluorescent tubes that are concealed in a specially built platform beneath it, appears to float on a pool of light. A pair of recessed downlighters give overhead light, and on the wall an uplighter with an opaline diffusing screen gives additional interest, creating a soft glow against the fluorescent background. A mirrored wall amplifies the effect. This is a good example of fluorescent lighting successfully used in a decorative, rather than practical, way.

Above. Four recessed downlighters with gold reflectors bring additional warmth to the rich colours of this bedroom — the soft golden tone of the light is sharply contrasted by the bright light of the adjoining white-walled bathroom. For bedside reading, a wall light has been fitted a little above and to the right of the bedhead. Known as the 'Decorator's Classic', this lamp has an adjustable brass arm, making it an ideal task light for the bedroom and elsewhere.

TASK LIGHTING

A good bedside light is the priority in a bedroom, with a switch close at hand for when you go to sleep and when you wake. It should be wired on a separate circuit from general and accent lights, ideally with controls at door as well as bedhead. Consider traditional table lamps, more contemporary portable fittings, and wall-mounted fittings placed just above, beside or on the bedhead. Whether you like symmetry or not, the conventional pair of lights, one each side, is a great convenience for double beds. Where one person in a double bed may want to read without disturbing a partner, the answer could be a small, modern task light with a narrow, adjustable beam, or a narrow-beam spotlight (of 10° or less); these could be directed precisely on to a book, shedding little light across the room.

Often task lighting is also needed for dressing table and mirrors. A full-length mirror is probably sufficiently well lit by the general light sources in the room. If necessary however, further light can be provided by adding one or two downlighters close to the face of the mirror or installing wall sconces left and right. Long, tungsten architectural strip-lamps placed vertically are ideal for this purpose. A single tungsten-halogen uplighter placed nearby would also be effective. At full brightness it provides strong daylight-toned light for making up, as long as the ceiling is a light colour; it can also be dimmed to provide softer general illumination. For the dressing table mirror, lights should also be placed on both left and right, at head level. These could be a pair of traditional table lamps or more modern sources. (See pp68-69 for more ideas on lighting mirrors.)

If the bedroom has large built-in cupboards it is probably necessary to illuminate the interiors. A long stretch of cupboard lends itself well to wall-washing. In most cases one fitting is required for each pair of cupboard doors, to ensure an even effect and adequate illumination of the contents. If the doors are pale in colour their surfaces will reflect enough light when closed to eradicate the need for any other general lighting — a good example of the combination of general and task functions. Built-in cupboards could also be lit by interior strip-lights controlled by door-operated switches; however this has the disadvantage of considerable expense in wiring and wasted energy if doors are left open. Another method, equally suitable for a freestanding piece, is to direct one or more eyeball fittings into the wardrobe.

Top right. A small table lamp makes a pretty, though impractical, light for the dressing table. Centre right. A trio of wall-washers light wardrobes evenly from top to bottom. Bottom right. Two bedside lights add to the low-level illumination from sources concealed beneath an acrylic strip at the back of built-in shelving.

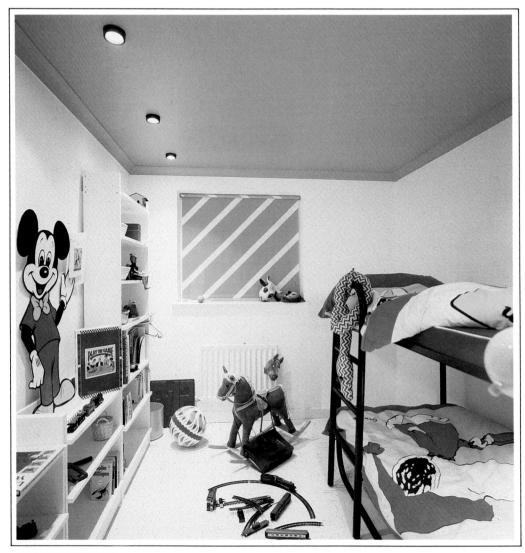

CHILDREN'S ROOMS

The needs of a child's room are quite different from those of an adult's bedroom. Moreover, the requirements will change as the child grows — a baby's bedroom will in time have to double as a schoolchild's study and a teenager's living room. The lighting plan will have to allow for all this.

The variety of activities that take place mean, first of all, that a higher level of general lighting will be required than for an adult's bedroom, a level equivalent to that of a living room or study. Secondly, the task lighting will have different priorities. It should be suitable for play and study as well as late-night reading. There should also be some source of soft lighting, important where there is a baby to be watched over or when a child is ill or just afraid of the dark. This can be

Above. Partially recessed, wide-beam downlighters give a soft-edged light to a realistically designed room. Their off-centre position brings extra light to the child's bookshelves and avoids glare over the bed. Right. Recessed eyeball downlighters and a strip-lamp give practical illumination while a note of fun is added by a drum uplighter and the low-wattage 'Suitcase' table lamp.

provided by a dimmer on a general or task fitting, or by a purpose-designed fitting, a modern equivalent to the traditional but dangerous candle night-light. Besides functional-looking, low wattage night-lights, it is possible to buy more fanciful lights, usually wall fittings, made from coloured plastic moulded into novel shapes — a cheery way to ward off the dark.

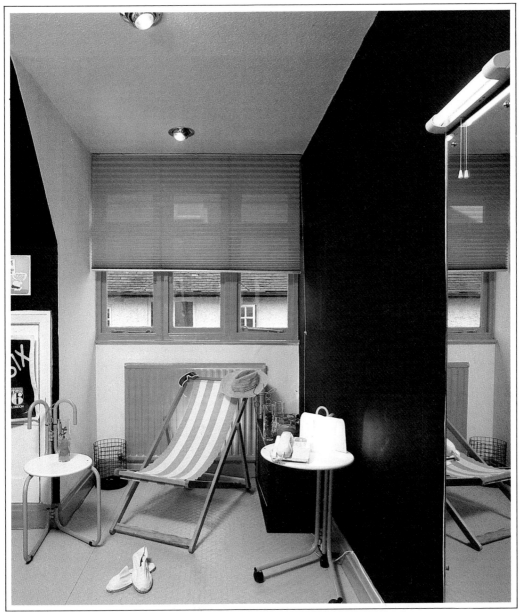

When selecting fittings for a child's room, or for any room in the house where a small child will have a free run, safety is a prime consideration. Avoid freestanding fittings that could be easily knocked over, and check for wires and workings that could be a danger to prying fingers. Keep as much as possible out of reach and try to ensure the quality of any products you buy: look for an authorized safety symbol. Finally, never allow complicated and potentially dangerous connections, avoid easily removable fittings and the use of adaptors.

Ideal fittings for a child's room, from nursery to teenage den, are eyeball fittings with wide-beam ISL or PAR bulbs, and track and spot arrangements. Both these types of lighting can be easily adjusted to suit new layouts, and are safely positioned on the ceiling, the eyeball being particularly impenetrable. Good all-purpose light but not such versatility could be provided by wall-mounted halogen uplighters. Special care should be taken to keep these out of reach because of the heat generated by a powerful tungsten-halogen bulb.

Lighting in the bathroom is as much of an expression of personal taste as in any other part of the house. The function of the room certainly presents a special set of lighting problems, but the answer need not be the standard, impersonal arrangement of purpose-designed fittings seen in so many homes. The effect could be bright and fresh for the early morning, shadier for long, luxurious baths, sparkling with a touch of Hollywood glamour, or a combination of all three. The requirements of the room will differ depending on whether it is a tiny, windowless capsule, a larger space with character of its own or an extension of the bedroom; whether it is for adults, children or the entire family.

Safety does of course set limitations on the design and use of light fittings in the bathroom, as the combination of water, steam and electricity is potentially dangerous. Regulations in the UK forbid the use of portable lamps of any

Above. In a sleek modern bathroom, fully recessed spill-ring downlighters are an effective, glare-free and safe source of general illumination. Their indirect light also gives an attractive sheen to the tiled walls. The mirror is lit separately by tungsten strip-lamps, which are concealed behind the built-in casing.

kind. Furthermore, they instruct that fittings should be sealed with glass or plastic covers, leaving no exposed metal that can be affected by steam and condensation. This excludes the use of most uplighters — except wall-mounted ones with a sealed top — all track and spot arrangements and some downlighters. Regulations also dictate the use of either a pull-cord switch inside the bathroom or of a wall switch outside; thus any dimmer switches must also be sited outside the room. Similarly, a pull-cord switch must be used for a light above a wash-basin in the bedroom.

Appropriate fittings are therefore the purpose-designed opaque discs, strips, globes and cubes — wall-mounted or ceiling-mounted — and certain types of downlighters, either ones with a PAR 38 bulb that has a specially toughened lens or ones with a reflector system and shielded bulb. Of the latter, spill-ring fittings are particularly effective since they minimize glare on the many shiny surfaces to be found in the bathroom — mirrors, porcelain, ceramic tiles, glossy paintwork. Spill-rings with gold reflectors can be used to give a warm touch, even to clinical, white-tiled walls and floors (see illustration on p15). Tungsten-halogen downlighters give the opposite effect. Wide-beam

Above. An unconventionally shaped array of low-voltage recessed downlighters, some directional, some non-directional, provides a crisp, bright light over the bath and on tapestry and flowers.

halogen fittings are appropriate near mirrors, narrow-beam ones over the bath or plants to give accent — the crisp, white output will sparkle on water, tiles and marble. Low-voltage downlighters are safest near water, not only because of their voltage but also because the transformer itself acts as an isolating device. For showers, suitable fittings are small, sealed sources and certain low-voltage downlighters with sealed glass covers.

TASK LIGHTING

Often the best scheme for a bathroom is an arrangement that combines general with task sources. This usually centres on the mirror, which is the most important point for task lighting in the room. If this is well illuminated, the rest of the general lighting does not need to reach a very high level; or if the room is very small, mirror lighting alone may be enough. A bathroom with good mirror lighting and more subdued sources elsewhere will appear far less utilitarian than one with high overall illumination.

Shaving, making up and cleaning teeth are all activities that call for very good light. With a bathroom mirror, as with a dressing-table mirror, the most effective strategy is to provide a pair of wide-beam sources left and right of the glass at eye level. This way, shadow on the face will be minimized. Both tungsten and fluorescent sources are widely available, the former producing a more flattering light, the latter a

Above. Paired wall fittings are a conventional form of mirror lighting. Below. In a dark-coloured room, it is necessary to use a pair of architectural strip-lamps each side of the mirror, plus downlighters above, to provide adequate illumination.

perhaps more truthful daylight tone. Suitable fittings are architectural strip-lamps, many of the purpose-made bathroom wall lights, or battens of balloon bulbs like those in theatre dressing rooms. The overpowering nature of a row of balloon bulbs can be resolved by using small, 40-watt, crown-silvered bulbs which reflect most of their light back on to the mirror and thus give a less direct output.

Other purpose-made bathroom fittings are designed to fit over the top of a small mirror above a single basin, or are even incorporated into the mirror. Besides being economical, these can be a neat and practical choice. Sources on

Above. Small 25-watt golf-ball bulbs make theatrical mirror lights, while a square recessed downlighter gives broader illumination.

the ceiling, either recessed or surface-mounted, can also be effectively used, but carry the danger that they may produce downward shadows on the face. However, if the mirror reaches the ceiling, the greater amount of light reflected indirectly into the room will reduce this problem. A useful extra can be an adjustable shaving mirror; many of these are now on the market with the choice of either a built-in light source or an extendible arm which can be angled to make the most of the existing light.

No-man's-lands or places of character? The hall, corridor and staircase are often given too little thought in terms of decorating, and left as nondescript areas through which to pass quickly from one area of the house to another. Yet they are central to the life of the house. The hall creates the initial impression and the corridors and stairs form vital connecting links through which people pass from room to room. Their decoration should harmonize with that of the adjoining rooms, asserting an overall style.

Their nature often makes these parts of the house architecturally interesting, offering unusual perspectives, changes of level and features such as archways and curving walls. All these elements lend themselves to interesting lighting effects. Moreover, in the relative absence of furniture in halls and other circulation areas, architectural features or the lighting itself can be the most important elements in the decorating scheme.

Below. Neat hall lighting is provided in a modern apartment by four recessed low-voltage sources: two downlighters and two directional fittings. Because a concrete ceiling made recessing impossible, the fittings are concealed in a specially built plywood box which has been positioned over an existing power outlet.

HALLS

Every hall needs good overall light. Moreover, that light must be produced by fittings that will neither impede circulation nor cause glare — particularly if, as in so many cases, stairs descend directly into the area. This makes ceiling-mounted fittings such as downlighters and wall-washers practical whereas freestanding uplighters often become a liability.

As the general level of lighting required is less than that required for rooms such as the kitchen or living room, it is often the practice to combine general with accent sources, particularly if the hall is small. For example, a wall-washer on one wall may easily be adequate. If it is used to illuminate a painting or hanging, perhaps on the wall facing the front door, it will also provide a welcoming touch of accent. Wide-beam eyeballs are another possibility, perhaps one directed on to a console table, one lighting the end wall, or one lighting the wall each side of the front door.

Suitable points for accenting in the hall could be furniture and pictures; but a particularly successful lighting strategy is to concentrate interest on entrance and exit, so that the wall facing the front door and that in which the front door is set are most important.

Large halls offer greater variety in treatment. Downlighting and wall-washing are again practical options, but there may be enough space to use freestanding fittings where these will not be in the way. Often a large hall possesses decorative architectural features such as high, elaborate ceilings and cornices which will benefit from dramatic uplighting. A wide space of open floor could be an ideal site for a fine rug enriched by a pool of downlighting. More traditionally, a large hall is an appropriate setting for a chandelier or decorative pendant, as these will be shown off to best advantage in

Above. Traditional picture lights, plus the glow from a downlighter on each half-landing of the staircase, give a welcoming atmosphere to the hall of a typical Victorian town house.

the absence of other visual distractions. The traditional plan is to add wall-brackets for supplementary lighting; however, more unusual results can be obtained with low-voltage accent sources. As in the living room, changes in atmosphere can then be generated by varying the levels of accent and general lighting for different times of day.

Above. A long, narrow corridor has a line of nine recessed low-voltage eyeball fittings, which are angled to produce a pattern against the curve of the barrelled ceiling. In the foreground, a pair of table lamps fitted with crown-silvered bulbs give a soft downward light.

Opposite. This unusually broad corridor is given separate points of emphasis by a variety of different light sources: a table lamp, a conventional picture light, and low-voltage narrow-beam spotlights directed on to display objects or vertically on to the marble floor.

CORRIDORS

For many people corridors evoke unpleasant connotations: dank and echoing in subways, tiled and antiseptic in hospitals, endless and anonymous in office buildings. They are a particular problem in many large apartments. While a single pendant will only emphasize the cheerless monotony of a corridor, a more sophisticated lighting scheme can break up the length and make it inviting to walk through, reclaiming a potentially gloomy area as an integral part of the house.

The basic rule for lighting corridors successfully is to have multiple fittings. A simple solution is to install a single length of track with small 40 or 60 watt spotlights which illuminate the walls alternately to left and right. If wide-beam,

ISL or similar bulbs are used (see *Bulb Chart*, pp88–89), the spots will provide practical illumination and also make a decorative pattern of scallops of light on the wall. A picture placed in each scallop would provide further interest for the eye. Similar effects could be achieved with downlighters spaced at intervals of 1.25–2m/4–6ft, or by using wall-mounted uplighters widely spaced so that they throw a pattern of light on to the ceiling and upper part of the walls. When lighting a corridor in this way, do not be afraid of creating dark patches. Because of its limited function, a corridor requires only approximately one third of the light level necessary for a living room. Thus a dramatic lighting scheme that uses strong contrasts of light and shade can still provide sufficient illumination.

STAIRCASES

Decoratively, the staircase lighting should be a continuation of the scheme adopted for the hallway. Yet it must also fulfil the practical function of permitting safe passage up and down. This means the lighting on the stairs must provide clear definition between each tread and riser. Over an open, sweeping staircase a strong source of light from the top will probably be sufficient. The more common 'dog-leg' staircase will require more attention as a source of light is necessary on each half-landing. Either a wide-beam downlighter or a pendant fitting could be used. Narrow-beam, low-voltage sources should be avoided since their output is too specific to give clear and safe illumination.

Likewise, it is a good idea to avoid the use of powerful uplighters such as the halogen types, which could cause glare when descending. Smaller uplighters using bulbs of less than 100 watts may, however, be acceptable, particularly if the bulb is shielded by some form of diffuser or louvre. Many of the wall-mounted uplighters, with their sleek shapes, give attractive visual punctuation to the wall, as do the more traditional wall lights and lanterns.

Below. A straightforward method of lighting any half-landing is ideal here for lighting the entrance to an apartment. A single surface-mounted downlighter with a PAR 38 bulb brings emphasis to the doorway as well as giving clear illumination on the steps.

Above. Low-voltage pin-spot sources (with 6° beam angles) send shafts of light down from the top of a narrow spiral staircase, bringing out the texture of the stone walls. A stained glass panel is lit from behind by two PAR 38 bulbs.

An open spiral staircase will generally receive enough light from the sources in the rooms through which it passes. In the case of a closed spiral staircase, it is worth taking time and trouble to provide lighting that will make the most of this uncommon architectural feature. Interesting patterns of light can be produced by positioning narrow-beam sources around the circumference at the top of the staircase so that their beams graze the walls; if two or three flights are involved, very narrow sources with a beam angle of only 6–10° will be needed. Alternatively, if there is sufficient space, a track could be mounted vertically on one wall and fitted with spotlights all the way up to throw beams of light at different angles.

It is conventional to have a two-way switch on each floor to allow control of the lights as one goes up and down the stairs. Many people, particularly those with young children, like to leave a light source on during the night. To lessen the waste of electricity, it is a good idea to fit dimmers to hall and staircase lighting schemes. Some modern dimmers have an integral 'time-lag' control which means that lights can be activated for a specific period only, after which they switch off automatically (see pp86–87).

Opposite. Recessed downlighters set into the underside of a staircase emphasize its sweeping form and brightly light the area below. The stairs themselves receive reflected light from walls and floor, supplemented by the wide accent beam directed on the picture, and by light from sources on the ceiling above.

In the garden, as in the house, the lighting can be divided up according to function: landscape lighting for night-time walks or for a vista to be viewed from inside the house; light for dining outside; light for showing the way and for security. Whatever the individual needs are, the most important point to remember is that, outdoors, a little light will go a long way. A helpful guide is to think of the dramatic effect produced by a simple battery-run torch: light from just a 3 or 4 watt bulb reaches for yards ahead. A torch pointed at a small bush or shrub will illuminate it beautifully. So a garden may be well lit by just a few light sources, provided they are judiciously selected and positioned. Fittings and wiring will be more costly than their indoor equivalents, but the fact that a small number of lights can produce an intriguing atmosphere is some compensation.

Above. Low-voltage spotlights using PAR 36 bulbs give pretty illumination in a town garden. The varied effect is produced by using a combination of fittings with different beam angles, all set on spikes in the planted-up containers.

GARDEN FEATURES

The rules for lighting the landscape elements of a garden, however large or small, are the same as those for all kinds of accent lighting: subjects should be chosen with restraint and lit with awareness of both form and contrast. An old tree, summer house, Gothic folly or Grecian temple if you have one, are obvious features for lighting; but think also of more subtle possibilities. Experiment with lighting plants in pots, plants rambling up walls and above all, white flowers; many of these, such as nicotiana and jasmine, are also highly scented at night.

Above. PAR 38 sources, some with blue colour filters, give dramatic landscape light.

There are various types of light fitting suitable for the domestic garden. For safety, all should be capable of withstanding the weather for many years; metalwork should be protected against corrosion and the bulb-holder and connectors should be completely sealed against moisture and dust. Because of the contrast with the surrounding darkness, the bulbs can be dazzling outdoors, so it is important that outdoor fittings have some form of glare control. Many are available with anti-glare cowls and louvres as standard accessories.

The most common and generally applicable fittings for the garden are ones that take the PAR 38 bulb, which is made from weatherproof, toughened glass. Most such fittings come with a plate for fixing on the wall or are mounted on a spike for positioning in flower beds, planters or lawns — the latter having the advantage that they can be moved to light different plants as they come into flower. Other fittings have a special clamp which can be fixed around a branch high in a tree — if these are used, ensure that the mount can be expanded to accommodate tree growth. Many different effects can be achieved with PAR 38s, given the variety of types and wattages available — spot and flood versions exist in each of 75, 100 and 150 watt ratings. For example, a 150 watt spot bulb might be positioned at the base of a tall tree and used to shine up through the foliage, or a wide-beam one might be used to illuminate plants close by. The yellowish tungsten light from the PAR 38 bulb is particularly attractive in the garden; it brings out the greens of foliage, and in autumn, the reds and golds.

Sources that take sodium and mercury vapour bulbs are more powerful. Sodium lighting produces the yellow colour most often seen in the floodlighting of castles and great houses, and is mainly used on this grand scale. Mercury vapour sources produce a distinctly blue light

Right. Close-up view of a PAR 38 outdoor spotlight with a spike base. It can be used with either spot or flood bulbs.

that is particularly effective on evergreens, and can make an interesting contrast with the light from tungsten sources elsewhere in the garden. The most useful type of fitting for both these kinds of bulb is the buried floodlight, which can be sunk in the ground amid a clump of trees or perhaps in the roots of one large tree. The output from these fittings depends on the reflector used, but usually has a beam angle in the order of 70°. To minimize glare, it is best to reserve these sources for dense areas of foliage or to corners and distant parts of the garden.

Low-voltage fittings using 12 volt PAR 36 bulbs are very successful for more subtle garden lighting. Their small size means that they can be discreetly hidden behind plants and pots, and the choice of narrow-spot, wide and very wide flood bulbs gives them versatility. As with low-voltage fittings indoors, however, transformers are needed in addition. Normally a group transformer is used to power several fittings, but it must be housed in a sheltered position and therefore long cable runs may be necessary to reach all the fittings. This means that special cable requirements are likely, all of which must be calculated carefully by the installer. Although installation is more complicated than with other fittings, low-voltage lighting offers the benefits of an almost total absence of glare and the minimum of visible hardware.

The house itself will dominate the garden landscape. Floodlighting it for effect, particularly if it stands well back from the road, can be a very welcoming sight. Most homes of no more than two or three storeys high can be lit by wide-beam PAR 38 fittings positioned at low level and 3–4m/10–13ft away from the façade. If the building is higher or extends more than 12–15m/40–50ft in width, more powerful floodlights will be needed and specialist help should be sought.

Above. PAR 38 fittings mounted on spikes within the shrubbery throw bright light across the path and steps. The front door is lit by a pair of wall lights which cast bold triangles of shadow above and below. Right. A futuristic luminous bollard makes a practical path light.

PATIOS, PATHS AND PORCHES

Areas immediately outside large window expanses, such as terraces and patios, require special lighting. This is necessary not only for practical reasons but also to provide easy transposition between house and garden, avoiding a stark break between bright light inside and the dark night outside. This can be achieved by lighting a flower bed or pot, small statue or plant, or by lighting an outdoor table. A table can be lit by traditional hurricane lamps or candles shielded from the wind, or by a PAR 38 spot mounted in a tree above or on a nearby wall. A wall or arbour overhung by a vine or other climber can be attractively lit by a PAR 38 spotlight concealed in the foliage. To create a festive atmosphere for parties or barbecues, ordinary PAR 38 bulbs can be replaced by coloured bulbs in red, blue or yellow; it is also possible to simply hire festoons of coloured bulbs on long leads, to drape over trees.

Below. A roof garden is well illuminated by light from indoors and from external spotlights.

Above. This modern building receives a dramatic night-time aspect from the combination of bright interior lighting with the bold exterior downlighting from a line of four wall-mounted fittings positioned on the main columns. A bollard light gives low-level illumination in the forecourt.

Paths and steps that are used at night may need task lighting. The traditional answer, the standard lantern, is decorative as an object but will give a wide, all-over output which can counteract and flatten a carefully considered lighting scheme. Instead, a wide range of specialized step lights, bollards and over-hanging pathway lights are available. These give practical lighting without detracting from the atmosphere.

Task lights are needed for gateways and for the front door. The traditional lantern, either hanging or wall-mounted, can be both attractive and efficient; more up-to-date alternatives include wall-mounted fittings that throw light both up and down, which can be particularly effective outside modern houses.

WATER AND SWIMMING POOLS

Water is one of the most exciting subjects for garden lighting. The shimmering blue depths of a swimming pool, for example, can look stunning at night. For really effective lighting, it is essential that the light sources are set into the sides of the pool itself and below the level of the water. This means that purpose-made submersible fittings should be installed, ideally when the pool is constructed, so that all wiring is kept completely out of the water. Most pool lights have 50-watt PAR 36 or 300-watt PAR 56 bulbs. Usually they are positioned to shine down the long length of the pool from the deep end.

Ornamental pools are also best lit by low-voltage sources submerged in the water, although ponds and larger expanses of still water can be well lit by rainproof floodlights just above water level, casting their light along the surface. Fountains are most dramatically lit by submerged narrow-beam sources set close to the base of each jet or shining along it so that the water sparkles as it is caught in the light. In the same way, waterfalls can be lit from behind so that light shines through the cascade.

Right. An enticing light comes from sources submerged in the water around the circumference of this pool. The patio is lit by a pair of lanterns.

Above. A pair of wall fittings that act as both uplighters and downlighters provide general illumination and emphasize an architrave. Left. Low-voltage narrow-beam downlighters set at the top of the pergola give a white light that enhances the pale stone of the columns and throws their reflections on to the water. Additional light comes from more low-voltage fittings, set within the hand-rail of the balustrading on the steps, and from PAR 38 fittings set among the plants by the house.

SECURITY

Security is the most purely practical function of outdoor lighting, and is often important for detached houses. It is possible to link the garden lighting to an alarm system so that it comes on to startle intruders, but it may just be enough to provide special lighting for some areas, such as car parks or the side of the house, which may not merit lighting for effect. In many cases a simple wall-mounted PAR 38 or a standard outdoor bulk-head fitting is adequate, positioned over garage or house doors, on the walls or corner of the house. If the area extends 9m/30ft in width or depth, a more effective solution would be a wall-fixed tungsten-halogen floodlight. These fit-tings take the linear tungsten-halogen bulbs used by domestic uplighters and are available in 200, 300 and 500 watt versions, all adapted for outdoor use. For maximum coverage, they should be mounted as high as possible on the wall. Although they are extremely efficient and will cover a large area, their bright, broad beam makes it inevitable that their output is totally flat, giving no distinction or relief. Thus security lighting of this nature should be planned and switched quite separately from the garden's decorative lighting.

INSTALLATION

All outdoor lighting should be installed by an approved electrical contractor; connections need to be properly sealed and wiring must be of a special type, set in conduit or buried. In view of the cost and labour involved in these safety measures, it is advisable to temporarily wire up one spotlight of each type that is intended to be used and check the exact position and effect before the contractor is commissioned. If only three or four PAR 38 fittings are required, it is possible to buy kits which are already correctly wired for external use. They have a long lead so that they can be plugged into a standard 13 amp socket in the house or garage.

When planning a garden lighting scheme, as with any plan for the garden, it is essential to look to the future: plants will grow, views will change from season to season and year to year. The plan should be most flexible around young plants, and any permanent sources that are complicated to install, such as buried floodlights, should be positioned beneath mature trees and shrubs where they will not be disturbed.

The more control a lighting scheme possesses, the better the results. In an all-purpose living area, for example, a multitude of different atmospheres can be generated if the general lighting can be dimmed separately from the accent lighting, and illumination of the dining table dimmed separately again. If just one dimmer is used for everything, changes in the level of brightness are possible but there can be no changes of emphasis.

A good system of control is achieved by providing separately switched wiring circuits for each group of light sources, or even individual sources, that fulfil a distinct type of function. This could be taken to the extreme of having ten separate switch circuits for each of ten fixtures within one room, but such a scheme would clearly be impractical to operate. The basic rule is to provide separate circuits for general, task and accent sources. Depending on the effects desired, these groups may be subdivided further. For example, where general lighting is provided by a combination of downlighters and chandelier, both types of fitting would benefit from installation on a separate circuit (see illustration on p35). Where uplighters and downlighters are used together, they too should ideally be switched separately, so that it is possible to play on their opposing effects. Within the accent lighting scheme, a key effect or object, such as a vase at the centre of a coffee table or a special painting, can be isolated for emphasis.

It is important to remember that not all types of light source are capable of being dimmed. Fluorescent sources can only be dimmed using sophisticated equipment requiring special wiring and not generally suitable for domestic use, and compact fluorescent sources cannot be dimmed at all.

MAKING A LIGHTING PLAN

A simple plan of the lighting layout is an invaluable aid both for working out the number of circuits required and later for instructing the electricians. To make one, first sketch the outline of the room, to scale if possible. Then, using the symbols shown opposite, mark the positions of ceiling and wall fittings, and of any 2-amp or 5-amp outlets that are intended to be centrally switched. Join up all groups of fittings or sockets which you wish to operate together with a single line, distinguished by a number or colour. The plan will probably show two or more circuits.

Having determined in this way how many circuits are needed, the next step is to choose from what points each circuit should be operated. Obvious switch positions are doorways, but it may also be appropriate to provide switches beside certain chairs or in a low-level position. Mark each control point on the plan with the correct symbol.

It is possible to install any number of on/off switches in one room, each overriding another as required. The majority of dimmers, however, are not so flexible; very often one switch acts exclusively as the dimming control while other switches provide on/off operation only, giving light at the level last set on the dimmer. This makes it important to decide where the dimming control will be most conveniently sited.

Typical circuits and switching requirements for lighting schemes in the house and garden

Living area	General: 1 or 2 dimmers Task: (occasional reading or study light) local switching Accent: 1 or 2 dimmers
Dining room	General: 1 dimmer Accent: 1 or 2 dimmers
Study/Work-room	General: 1 dimmer Task: local switching Accent: 1 dimmer
Kitchen	General: 1 dimmer Task: (under cupboards) switch only; (other) local switching Accent (dining area): 1 dimmer
Bedroom	1 or 2 dimmers, depending on whether general and accent lighting have separate focuses; two-way switching
Bathroom	General: 1 dimmer (outside room) Task: local switching (pull-cord operated)
Hall/Staircase/ Corridor	Switching at each level or access point; possibly dimmers and time-lag devices
Garden	Dimming not usually necessary

Opposite. Lighting plan for a living room. The room, on a typical period plan with large fireplace and bay window, is lit by a combination of traditional and modern sources. One circuit (in blue) contains transformers and links up all the low-voltage fittings. These include three pairs of low-voltage recessed downlighters — used to cross-light a picture above the mantelpiece, to highlight a pair of urns either side of the fireplace, and to cross-light a picture on the wall behind one sofa — and also a single low-voltage recessed downlighter over the coffee table. A second circuit (in red) links a pair of wall sconces, table lamps which plug into floor sockets, and a portable drum uplighter. The third circuit (in yellow) powers an array of recessed wall-washers.

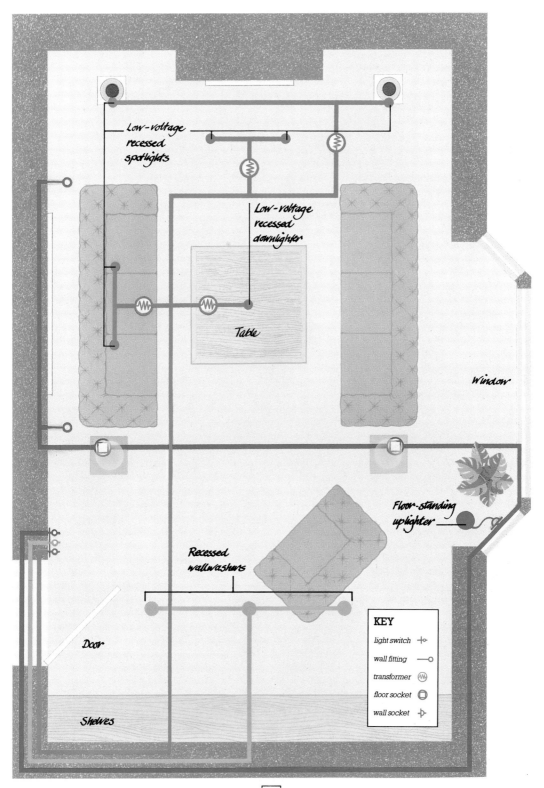

Low-voltage recessed spotlights

Low-voltage recessed downlighter

Table

Window

Floor-standing uplighter

Recessed wallwashers

Door

Shelves

KEY

light switch   +∘

wall fitting   —∘

transformer   ⓦ

floor socket   ▢

wall socket   ⊸

The open-plan house shown on these pages was given eight different lighting circuits within the main space, separating the lighting as well as the function of the different living areas. *Above and left.* General lighting for the kitchen is provided by four recessed eyeballs (circuit 1), while a track-mounted spotlight highlights the sculpture on the counter (circuit 2). Beyond the kitchen, recessed directional downlighters (unseen) have been fitted to light the dining area (circuit 3). *Opposite, top.* The gallery bedroom receives dramatic lighting from track fittings and from wall-washers on the blinds (circuit 4). A small hallway (far right) is lit by a downlighter (circuit 5). *Opposite, bottom.* The sitting area, its atmosphere and focal points quite different by night and by day, receives light from table lamps (circuit 6), a drum uplighter in the large arched window (circuit 7), and track lighting over the coffee table (circuit 8). This division of circuits gives the user control of the space, making it possible to emphasize or lose each area at will.

DIMMERS

Dimmers are essential for flexible lighting. Contrary to what might be expected, dimmers do not provide significant energy savings; however, their use can greatly lengthen bulb life, particularly if the bulbs are always used at a range of intensities, that is, dimmed up and down rather than kept at the same level and merely switched on and off. The table below gives an indication of these factors.

Savings achieved by dimming

Light output %	Power saving %	Bulb life increase factor
100	0	× 1
90	6	× 1.6
70	16	× 4.2
40	35	× 36

Below, top left. 'Slider Dimmer', with rocking on/off switch and separate, sliding dimming control. It can be switched on or off at any brightness. Load rating: 60–630 watts. Top right. Security control switch. It automatically switches on at dusk and off after a preset period of between one and eight hours. A neon indicator shows when the switch is activated. Load rating: 60–400 watts. Bottom. Twin dimmer switches which combine push switching and rotary action dimming control. These switches can be one or two-way. Load rating: two circuits, each 40–250 watts.

There are many different types of dimmer on the market. The standard types offer rotary operation, that is, the dimmer clicks 'on' when the knob is turned clockwise and the light level increases as the knob is turned further. This type cannot be used in conjunction with another switch elsewhere in the room.

The 'push-on, push-off' type overcomes this problem. These dimmers have a knob that is pressed down to generate on/off functions but is turned to adjust brightness. Although two-way switching is possible with this type, dimming control is restricted to a single switch. When the lights are put off, the dimmer is left set at the lighting level last used.

More sophisticated electronic devices are available which offer dimming control from each switch position; many of these are operated simply by touch. There are also some which offer control from a hand-held infra-red device. Some dimmers and switches incorporate time-lag devices whereby lights switch off automatically after a predetermined time.

In view of the vast variety of types of dimmer available, it is advisable to consult an electrician, specialist shop or manufacturer before making a purchase. Presentation of the lighting plan for each room will give them a clear picture of the switching requirements so that they can give advice on the most appropriate control system.

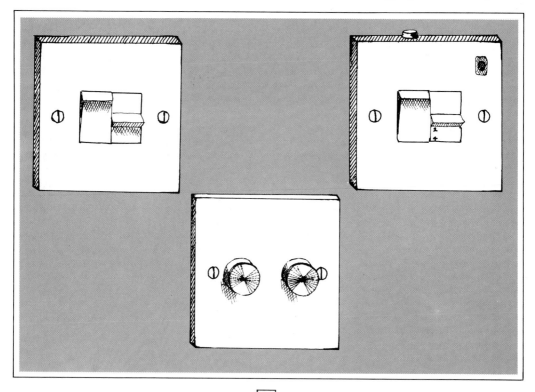

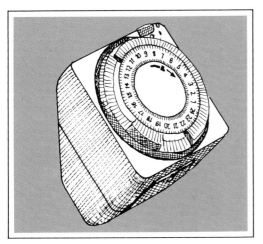

TECHNICAL CONSIDERATIONS

The most important technical factor to consider in the installation of all control devices is the rating of the *load*. The load is the sum total of all the wattages of the bulbs on the circuit to be controlled. For example, three 100-watt bulbs would constitute a 300-watt load. In every case the rating of the control device must at least match, if not exceed, that of the load it is to operate. It is important to check the total wattage of the fittings rather than the bulbs chosen for them. It is a mistake to match the rating of the dimmer to three 60-watt bulbs if the fittings will accept, and may later be fitted with, 100-watt bulbs; the excessive wattage would cause the control to fail.

Low-voltage sources must be used with a dimmer that is marked as having been adapted for what is described as an *inductive* load. This takes account of the fact that a transformer is included in the circuit.

Where six or more circuits are used in one room, it may be worthwhile commissioning a custom-made fully electronic dimming system. This involves special wiring but offers the sophistication of a programme that can control a series of different lighting scenes. Changes of light level can be set to happen over a prescribed number of seconds, and operated by a momentary touch of a button.

Above. Security timer. It plugs into a standard 13-amp socket and includes its own socket outlet for table lamps. It will switch on and off at preset times. Below left. Multiple dimmer, with push switching and rotary dimming control, set in a brass switch-plate. Load rating: four circuits, each 60–400 watts. Right. Touch dimmer. A quick touch operates on and off; further touches adjust brightness. Touch dimmers allow you to dim as well as switch from multiple positions. Load rating: 40–250 or 60–630 watts. Bottom. 'In-line' dimmer which fits on to the cable of a table or standard lamp.

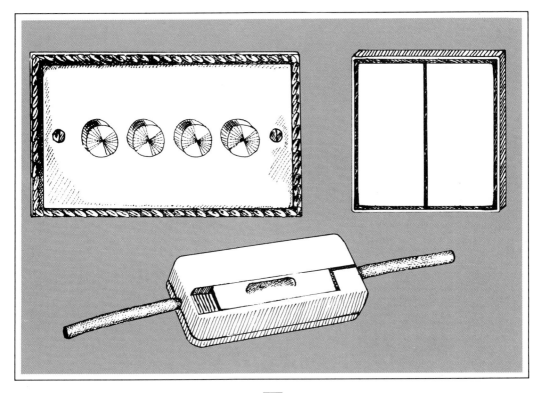

The chart below gives specifications for the major types of light bulb suitable for domestic use. It aims to give a representative selection of the range currently available; however details will vary according to manufacturer, and new beam angles and wattages are constantly being introduced.

When ordering, it is important to remember that in the trade a light bulb is referred to as a 'lamp'.

Notes
1. *Bulb caps* are coded to correspond to the socket in the light fitting. The commonest cap types are the bayonet cap (BC) and the Edison Screw (ES).
2. *Safety distance* indicates how far the bulb should be placed from objects to prevent scorching.

Type	Description	Wattage	Voltage	Cap	Mean life	Beam angle	Safety distance
TUNGSTEN							
	GLS	40	240	E27/BC	1000 hours		0.5m/1½ft
	(General Lighting	60	240	E27/BC	1000 hours		0.5m/1½ft
	Service)	100	240	E27/BC	1000 hours		0.5m/1½ft
		150	240	E27/BC	1000 hours		0.8m/2½ft
		200	240	E27/BC	1000 hours		0.8m/2½ft
	Golf-ball (also called 'spherical' or 'balloon' bulb)	40	240	E14/BC	1000 hours		0.5m/1½ft
	Globe	25	240	E27	2000 hours		
		40	240	E27	2000 hours		
		60	240	E27	2000 hours		
		100	240	E27	2000 hours		
		150	240	E27	2000 hours		
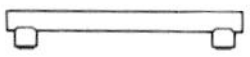	Architectural strip-light (also called 'linear' bulb)	35	240	S14s	1000 hours		
		60	240	S14s	1000 hours		
		120	240	S14s	1000 hours		
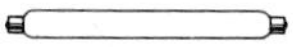	Standard strip-light	30	240	S15s	1000 hours		
		60	240	S15s	1000 hours		
	PAR 36 Parabolic aluminized reflector bulb)	25	12	Screw	2000 hours	8°×10°	0.8m/2½ft
		50	12	Screw	2000 hours	9°×11°	0.8m/2½ft
		30	6	Screw	1000 hours	3.5°	0.5m/1½ft
	PAR 38 spot	75	240	E27	2000 hours	15°	0.5m/1½ft
	flood	75	240	E27	2000 hours	40°	0.5m/1½ft
	spot	100	240	E27	2000 hours	15°	0.5m/1½ft
	flood	100	240	E27	2000 hours	40°	0.5m/1½ft
	spot	150	240	E27	2000 hours	15°	0.8m/2½ft
	flood	150	240	E27	2000 hours	40°	0.8m/2½ft
	spot	60	240	E27	2000 hours	12°	0.5m/1½ft
	flood	60	240	E27	2000 hours	30°	0.5m/1½ft
	spot	80	240	E27	2000 hours	12°	0.5m/1½ft
	flood	80	240	E27	2000 hours	30°	0.5m/1½ft
	spot	120	240	E27	2000 hours	12°	0.8m/2½ft
	flood	120	240	E27	2000 hours	30°	0.8m/2½ft
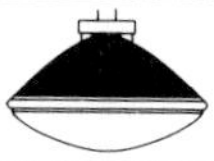	PAR 56 narrow-beam	300	240	G×16d	2000 hours	10°×16°	1.4m/4½ft
	medium-beam	300	240	G×16d	2000 hours	13°×26°	1.1m/3½ft
	wide-beam	300	240	G×16d	2000 hours	18°×34°	0.8m/2½ft
	ISL (Internally silvered reflector bulb)	40	240	E14/E27	1000 hours	35°	0.5m/1½ft
		60	240	E27	1000 hours	80°	0.5m/1½ft
		60	240	E27	1000 hours	35°	0.5m/1½ft
		75	240	E27	1000 hours	35°	0.5m/1½ft
		75	240	E27	1000 hours	100°	0.5m/1½ft
		100	240	E27	1000 hours	35°	0.5m/1½ft
		150	240	E27	1000 hours	35°	0.8m/2½ft
	Crown-silvered bulb	40	240	E14	1000 hours		0.5m/1½ft
		60	240	E27	1000 hours		0.5m/1½ft
		100	240	E27	1000 hours		0.8m/2½ft

BULB CHART

Type	Description	Wattage	Voltage	Cap	Mean life	Beam angle	Safety distance
TUNGSTEN-HALOGEN							
	Low-voltage tungsten-halogen reflector bulbs	20	12	G4	2000 hours	10°	0.5m/1½ft
		20	12	G4	2000 hours	15°	0.5m/1½ft
		35	6	Bal5d	2000 hours	6°	0.8m/2½ft
		35	6	Bal5d	2000 hours	14°	0.8m/2½ft
		20	12	Bal5d	1000 hours	18°×32°	0.5m/1½ft
		20	12	Bal5d	2000 hours	10°×25°	0.5m/1½ft
		20	12	Bal5d	2000 hours	6°	0.5m/1½ft
	Tungsten-halogen bulb with metal reflector	50	12	Bal5d	2000 hours	10°	0.5m/1½ft
		50	12	Bal5d	2000 hours	30°	0.5m/1½ft
	Multi-mirror	20	12	G×5.3	3000 hours	7°×5°	
		20	12	G×5.3	3000 hours	13°×10°	
		20	12	G×5.3	3000 hours	36°×37°	
		50	12	G×5.3	3000 hours	13°×11°	
		50	12	G×5.3	3000 hours	27°×22°	
		50	12	G×5.3	3000 hours	31°×37°	
		75	12	G×5.3	3000 hours	15°×14°	
		75	12	G×5.3	3000 hours	38°×40°	
	Low-voltage tungsten-halogen bulb	20	12	G4	2000 hours		0.5m/1½ft
		50	12	GY6.35	2000 hours		0.5m/1½ft
		100	12	GY6.35	2000 hours		0.5m/1½ft
		20	24	G4	2000 hours		0.5m/1½ft
		50	24	GY6.35	2000 hours		0.5m/1½ft
		100	24	GY6.35	2000 hours		0.5m/1½ft
	Tubular tungsten-halogen bulb	100	240	E27	2000 hours		
		150	240	E27	2000 hours		
		250	240	E27	2000 hours		
	Linear tungsten-halogen bulb	100	240	R7s	1000 hours		
		150	240	R7s	1000 hours		
		200	240	R7s	1000 hours		
		300	240	R7s	1500 hours		
		500	240	R7s	2000 hours		

Type	Description	Wattage	Voltage	Cap	Diameter	Length	Mean life
FLUORESCENT	Standard (triphosphor or halophosphate)	15	220	G13	26mm/1in	450mm/18in	7000 hours
		30	220	G13	26mm/1in	900mm/3ft	7000 hours
		20	220	G13	26mm/1in	600mm/2ft	7000 hours
		18	220	G13	26mm/1in	600mm/2ft	7000 hours
		40	220	G13	26mm/1in	1200mm/4ft	7000 hours
		36	220	G13	26mm/1in	1200mm/4ft	7000 hours
		65	220	G13	26mm/1in	1500mm/5ft	7000 hours
		58	220	G13	26mm/1in	1500mm/5ft	7000 hours
		75/85	220	G13	26mm/1in	1800mm/6ft	7000 hours
		70	220	G13	26mm/1in	1800mm/6ft	7000 hours
		125	220	G13	26mm/1in	2400mm/8ft	7000 hours
		100	220	G13	26mm/1in	2400mm/8ft	7000 hours
	Miniature	4	220	G5/15	16mm/½in	150mm/6in	5000 hours
		6	220	G5/15	16mm/½in	225mm/9in	5000 hours
		8	220	G5/15	16mm/½in	300mm/12in	7500 hours
		13	220	G5/15	16mm/½in	525mm/21in	7500 hours
	Compact	7	240	G23			5000 hours
		9	240	G23			5000 hours
		11	240	G23			5000 hours
		18	240	G23			5000 hours
		24	240	G23			5000 hours
		35	240	G23			5000 hours

Accent light
Gives local rather than general illumination and is used to create visual focal points and to emphasize objects; it is supplementary to the general lighting scheme.

Amp
An abbreviation of ampere, an internationally agreed unit of electric current.

Baffle
A device attached to a light fitting that helps to prevent glare.

Beam angle
Measure of the spread of illumination obtained from a reflector bulb or fitting. It is calculated as twice the angle between the centre of the light beam and the point where the light level drops to one half the intensity at the centre.

Bulk-head fitting
A tough metal-and-glass wall fitting, suitable for either outdoor or indoor lighting.

Cold-cathode light
Technical term for *neon light*

Compact fluorescent bulb
A small bulb, such as the *Philips PL* or *Thorn 2D*, available in a variety of shapes and operating on the same principle as a *fluorescent tube*. The bulbs can be used in a wide variety of fittings; however they cannot be dimmed.

Cross-lighting
A way of accenting a picture, plant or ornament by lighting it from two different directions.

Crown-silvered bulb
An *incandescent, tungsten, reflector bulb* that has an internally silvered, reflective front surface. This causes light to be thrown in one direction only, producing a sharply defined beam.

Dichroic
A term applied to certain types of bulb (e.g. *multi-mirror low-voltage* sources) which is designed to pass the majority of its heat output backwards, in the opposite direction to the beam of light.

Downlighter
A light fitting that casts light directly downwards; usually mounted or recessed in the ceiling.

Drum uplighter
A compact, low-intensity *uplighter*, primarily intended for accent lighting.

Eyeball fitting
A semi-recessed, directional downlighter; it has a spherical base that can be swivelled in its socket so that light is directed at an angle, as from a *spotlight*.

Fluorescent tube
A light source composed of a glass tube that is coated with fluorescent phosphor powders and contains an inert gas such as argon, krypton or neon, and mercury vapour at low pressure. When electricity is passed through the tube the phosphorous layer is excited and emits light.

Framing projector
A *low-voltage* fitting that is specially designed for accent lighting; it has a system of lenses and shutters that can shape the light beam exactly to the outline of the picture or object that is being highlighted.

GLS bulb
General Lighting Service bulb, trade term for the standard *incandescent* light bulb.

Grolux tube
A *fluorescent tube* with a mauve-coloured output that can be used to grow plants in the complete absence of any other light.

Halogen bulb
Common term for *tungsten-halogen bulb*.

Incandescent bulb
A bulb which produces light as a result of heating a tungsten filament by an electric current.

Inductive load
Describes a *load* in a circuit that incorporates a *transformer*.

ISL bulb
An internally silvered *reflector bulb*, with the silvering on the back surfaces (rather than the crown) of the bulb.

Load
The sum total of the wattages of all the bulbs used in a circuit.

Low-voltage bulb
A miniature bulb that runs on 12 or 24 volts rather than mains voltage (240 in UK/100 in USA); it requires a *transformer* to step down the voltage. These bulbs provide more precise optical control and produce less heat than conventional mains-voltage bulbs.

Lux
An internationally agreed unit used to measure the amount of light falling on any surface.

Mercury-vapour bulb
A bulb which contains mercury vapour at low pressure and produces a greenish-blue light when electricity is passed through it; commonly used for outdoor lighting.

Metal-halide bulb
A bulb which contains metal halides in a quartz discharge tube, producing an extremely efficient white light with very good colour rendering; used commercially and for outdoor floodlighting.

Multi-mirror bulb
A miniature *low-voltage bulb* that has an integral multi-faceted reflector.

Neon light
A tube containing the inert gas neon at low pressure, which emits a reddish, glowing light when electricity is passed through it. The name is also commonly applied to similar tubes containing argon or krypton gases.

PAR bulb
A parabolic aluminized reflector bulb, which incorporates its own reflector to direct a powerful beam of light. As the name implies, it is parabolic in cross-section, internally aluminized and made of heat-resistant glass.

Philips PL bulb
A *compact fluorescent bulb* made by Philips in the UK; it is suitable for use in wall, ceiling or task fittings.

Reflector bulb
A variety of bulbs such as the *PAR 38, ISL* or *multi-mirror* that incorporate their own reflectors to direct light outwards.

Scoop reflector
An additional, broadly curved reflector in a wall-washer which ensures that light is spread to the top of the wall.

Sodium bulb
A bulb containing neon and sodium vapour at low pressure, producing an orange-coloured light when electricity is passed through it; used in floodlights and street lamps.

Spotlight
Term which loosely describes a variety of purpose-designed sources that produce a directional light beam, suitable as *accent lights*.

Task light
A light fitting designed and used for a specific localized function.

Thorn 2D bulb
A *compact fluorescent bulb* used in wall, ceiling and *task light* fittings. It is manufactured by Thorn EMI.

Track
A length of insulated conductor on to which light fittings can be clipped. Versions exist for carrying one, two, three or four different circuits.

Transformer
A device that steps down the domestic electricity supply from mains voltage to the required low voltage. It is an essential component in the installation of any kind of low-voltage source.

Tungsten bulb
A bulb containing a tungsten filament; also called an *incandescent bulb*.

Tungsten strip-light
A linear, *incandescent* fitting with a tungsten filament running through a tube rather than a conventional bulb shape.

Tungsten-halogen bulb
A tungsten-filament bulb containing a halogen gas filling. The halogen gas combines with tungsten to create a far brighter light than an equivalent *wattage tungsten bulb* would give, and also prolongs bulb life. Tungsten-halogen bulbs are sometimes referred to as quartz-halogen bulbs or simply *halogen* bulbs.

Uplighter
A light fitting that directs light upwards on to the ceiling, illuminating the room by reflection; usually wall-mounted or freestanding.

Va rating
Measure of the capacity of a *transformer* in terms of the *wattage* of the bulbs which may be connected to it.

Volt
A unit expressing the potential of an electrical circuit.

Wall-washer
Light fitting designed to cast light evenly across and down a wall, using the wall as a reflector; usually ceiling-mounted.

Watt
A unit of power used to describe the energy produced by an electrical appliance; in a light bulb, it describes the light output.

British Standards safety mark
When this symbol is shown on a light fitting it indicates that the product satisfies UK and EEC regulations regarding the safety of electrical luminaires.

Space permits only a selection of lighting manufacturers, distributors and retail outlets to be included here. The majority of the companies listed specialize in modern lighting, and all the specialist shops have staff who are willing to advise on installation. Information was correct at the time of going to press.

* indicates that the shop also provides a consultancy service.

Manufacturers and distributors of fittings

Argon Neon Ltd. 17 Neal St, London WC2; tel: (01) 240 5051. *Neon lighting off-the-peg or made to order.*

Artemide GB Ltd. 17 Neal St, London WC2; tel: (01) 240 2346. *Stylish pendant and portable fittings.*

Anglepoise Lighting Ltd. Enfield Industrial Estate, Redditch B97 6DR; tel: (0527) 63771. *Specialists in adjustable task lights.*

Best & Lloyd Ltd. William St West, Smethwick, Warley, West Midlands; tel: (021) 558 1191. *Picture lights and brass fittings.*

C & R Lighting Systems. Southfields Rd, Dunstable, Beds LU6 3EJ; tel: (0582) 62423. *Track systems.*

Candlelight Graphix Ltd. Vauxhall Place, Lowfield St, Dartford, Kent DA1 1HU; tel: (0322) 22389. *Specialists in decorative lighting made from plastic strips containing miniature bulbs.*

Concord Lighting Ltd. Rotaflex House, 241 City Road, London EC1V 1JD; tel: (01) 253 1200. *Track fittings, spotlights, downlighters, low-voltage, fluorescents etc; some garden fittings.*

Crompton Parkinson Ltd. Woodlands House, The Avenue, Cliftonville, Northampton NN1 5BS; tel: (0604) 30201. *Spotlights, downlighters, fluorescent fittings etc; commercial lighting specialists.*

Erco Lighting Ltd. 38 Dover St, London W1X 3RB; tel: (01) 408 0320. *Spotlights, downlighters, track systems, fluorescents, low-voltage etc.*

Flos. Heath Hall, Heath, Wakefield WF1 5SL; tel: (0924) 366446. *Stylish modern pendant and portable fittings.*

Forma/Victor Mann & Co Ltd. *Unit 3, Mitcham Industrial Estate, 85 Streatham Rd, Mitcham, Surrey CR4 2AD; tel: (01) 640 6811. Distributors for iGuzzini, C.I.L. (Italy); track, pendant and portable fittings.*

Futimis. Kings Cottage, Kings Hill, Loughton, Essex IG10 1HY; tel: (01) 502 0134. *Uplighters, low-voltage fittings, metal-halide lights, fluorescent tube systems.*

Hitech (UK) Ltd. Tower House, Lea Valley Trading Estate, Edmonton, London N18 3HR; tel: (01) 884 3333. *Low-voltage lighting.*

Lita Display Ltd. 190 City Road, London EC1V 2QR; tel: (01) 251 8844. *Fluorescent, incandescent and low-voltage systems; portable and pendant fittings.*

Marlin Lighting Ltd. Hanworth Trading Estate, Hampton Rd West, Feltham, Miiddlesex TW13 6DR; tel: (01) 894 5522. *Track systems, downlighters, modern chandeliers.*

Mole-Richardson (England) Ltd. 62-66 Whitfield St, London W1P 6JH; tel: (01) 636 3636. *Low-voltage lighting.*

Omega Lighting. Albany House, Burlington Rd, New Malden, Surrey KT3 4NJ; tel: (01) 363 5353. *Thorn EMI subsidiary handling lighting for retail: spotlights, energy-saving fittings, fluorescents, garden lighting, also downlighters, low-voltage lighting.*

Philips Lighting Ltd. City House, 420-430 London Rd, Croydon CR9 3QR; tel: (01) 689 2166. *Fluorescent fittings, spotlights, downlighters, floodlights etc.*

Prima Lighting. 151 Deans Lane, Edgware, Middlesex HD8 9N7; tel: (01) 959 0277. *Recessed, fluorescent, halogen and low-voltage fittings.*

Rotaflex Homelighting. Malmesbury, Wiltshire SN16 0BN; tel: (066) 62 2001. *Spotlights, downlighters.*

Shiu Kay Khan. 90 Belsize Lane, London NW3 5BE; tel: (01) 431 0451. *Modern designer lighting.*

Spectrum. 122 Drury Lane, London WC2B 5SU; tel: (01) 835 1104. *Distributors for AB Bruno Herbst (Sweden); fluorescent fittings.*

Sunlight Systems. Unit 148, Stratford Workshops, Burford Rd, London E15 2SP; tel: (01) 519 2251. *Plant growth lamps.*

Specialist lighting shops

John Cullen Lighting Design. Woodfall Court, Smith St, London SW3; tel: (01) 352 3566.*

Designed Lighting. Bridge House, 129 Station Rd, Hayes, Middlesex; tel: (01) 561 1193.*

Electromode. 1 Old Eldon Square, Newcastle 1; tel: (0632) 321326.

Exchange Electrical Lighting Ltd. 48-52 Cheetham Hill Rd, Manchester 4; tel: (061) 834 4259.

Extralite Designs Ltd. 26 Northways Parade, College Crescent, London NW3; tel: (01) 722 7480.

Into Lighting. 49 High St, Wimbledon Village, London SW19; tel: (01) 946 8533.*

The Lighting Workshop. 35-6 Floral St, London WC2; tel: (01) 241 0461.*

Lightolier Ltd. 28-30 Bristol St, Birmingham 5; tel: (021) 622 4932/4096.

London Lighting Co Ltd. 135 Fulham Rd, London SW3; tel: (01) 589 3612.

Marcatré. 179 Shaftesbury Avenue, London WC2; tel: (01) 379 6865.

Mr Light. 307 Brompton Rd, London SW3; tel: (01) 581 3470.

New Lighting Centre. 62 Scotswood Rd, Newcastle; tel: (0632) 328043.*

New Lites. 7 Village Way East, Rayners Lane, Harrow, London HA2 7LX; tel: (01) 866 6177.

Nova Lighting. 71 Candelriggs, Glasgow; tel: (041) 552 7324.*

Pagazzi Interior Lighting. 106 West George St, Glasgow G2 1PS; tel: (051) 647 9472.*

Universal Lighting Services Ltd. Priory St, Birkenhead; tel: (041) 333 0882.*

West Midland Lighting Centre. 10-12 York Rd, Erdington, Birmingham B23 6TE; tel: (021) 350 1999.

CREDITS

The credits list page number and, if two or more pictures on a page were obtained from different sources, the position of each picture, then the source (photographer, picture agency or fitting manufacturer), and lastly, additional credits for lighting or interior design.

P6 Michael Dunne, lighting/John Cullen; *p7* Robert Belton, lighting/John Cullen; *pp8-9* illustration/Richard Draper; *pp10-11* Robert Belton, lighting/John Cullen; *p12* Elizabeth Whiting & Associates; *p13* Concord Lighting Ltd; *p14* diagrams/Graham Rosewarne; *p15 top* Robert Belton, lighting/John Cullen, *bottom* Concord Lighting Ltd; *p16 top* Concord Lighting Ltd; *centre and bottom* Erco Lighting Ltd; *p17* Concord Lighting Ltd; *p18* Mr Light; *p19* Michael Dunne, lighting/John Cullen; *p20* Artemide GB Ltd; *p21 top left* Anglepoise Lighting Ltd, *top right and bottom right* The Lighting Workshop, *bottom left* Artemide GB Ltd; *p22* Robert Belton, lighting/John Cullen; *p23 top left, centre and right* Concord Lighting Ltd, *right* diagram/Graham Rosewarne; *p24* Robert Belton, lighting/John Cullen; *p25 top* Osram (GEC) Ltd, *bottom left and right* Erco Lighting Ltd; *p26* Concord Lighting Ltd; *p27 top left and right* Mole-Richardson (England) Ltd, *bottom* Robert Belton, lighting/John Cullen; *p28 top* Elizabeth Whiting & Associates, *bottom* Robert Belton, lighting/John Cullen; *p29 top* Elizabeth Whiting & Associates, *bottom* Erco Lighting Ltd; *p30 top* Elizabeth Whiting & Associates, *bottom* Jan Carter, Los Angeles Neon; *p31* Argon Neon Ltd, fitting design/Basham & Ughetti; *p32* Concord Lighting Ltd; *p33* Michael Dunne, design/Nilly Stanley; *p34* Artemide GB Ltd; *p35* Robert Belton, lighting/John Cullen; *p36* Elizabeth Whiting & Associates; *pp37-39* Robert Belton, lighting/John Cullen; *p40* Elizabeth Whiting & Associates; *pp41-43* Robert Belton, lighting/John Cullen; *p44* Michael Dunne, design/Diana Phipps; *pp45-46* Elizabeth Whiting & Associates; *p47* Robert Belton, lighting/John Cullen; *p48* Artemide GB Ltd; *p49 top* Michael Dunne, design Earl Burn Combs, *right* Robert Belton, lighting/John Cullen; *p50* Elizabeth Whiting & Associates; *p51 top* Michael Dunne, design/Joanna Wood, *bottom* Elizabeth Whiting & Associates; *p52 top* Elizabeth Whiting & Associates, *bottom* Spectrum; *pp54-55* Elizabeth Whiting & Associates; *pp56-57* Robert Belton, lighting/John Cullen; *p58* Michael Dunne, design/Michael Dunne; *p59 top* Michael Dunne, design/Borus & Borus, *bottom* Robert Belton, lighting/John Cullen; *pp60-62* Robert Belton, lighting/John Cullen; *p63 top and centre* Robert Belton, lighting/John Cullen, *bottom* Elizabeth Whiting & Associates; *p64* Concord Lighting Ltd; *p65* Roma Jay Kitchen Consultants; *pp66-67* Robert Belton, lighting/John Cullen; *p68* Concord Lighting Ltd; *pp69-72* Robert Belton, lighting/John Cullen; *p73* Michael Dunne, design/Borus & Borus; *p74 top* Robert Belton, lighting/John Cullen, *bottom* Concord Lighting Ltd; *p75* Erco Lighting Ltd; *p76* Robert Belton, lighting/John Cullen; *pp77-78* Concord Lighting Ltd; *p79* Elizabeth Whiting & Associates; *p80 top* Elizabeth Whiting & Associates, *bottom* Robert Belton, lighting/John Cullen; *p81* Concord Lighting Ltd; *p83* diagram/Graham Rosewarne; *pp84-85* Robert Belton, lighting/John Cullen; *pp86-87* illustration/Clare Finlaison.
Information and drawings for the *Bulb Chart* were kindly supplied by Erco Lighting Ltd, with additional material from Concord Lighting Ltd.